New
ENGLISH FILE
CULTURE LINK

OXFORD
UNIVERSITY PRESS

OXFORD
UNIVERSITY PRESS

Great Clarendon Street, Oxford OX2 6DP

Oxford University Press is a department of the University of Oxford.
It furthers the University's objective of excellence in research, scholarship,
and education by publishing worldwide in

Oxford New York

Auckland Cape Town Dar es Salaam Hong Kong Karachi
Kuala Lumpur Madrid Melbourne Mexico City Nairobi
New Delhi Shanghai Taipei Toronto

With offices in

Argentina Austria Brazil Chile Czech Republic France Greece
Guatemala Hungary Italy Japan Poland Portugal Singapore
South Korea Switzerland Thailand Turkey Ukraine Vietnam

OXFORD and OXFORD ENGLISH are registered trade marks of
Oxford University Press in the UK and in certain other countries

© Oxford University Press 2011

ISBN: 978 0 19 459595 7   Workbook
ISBN: 978 0 19 459596 4   Pack
ISBN: 978 0 19 459594 0   DVD
ISBN: 978 0 19 451940 3   Audio CD

Printed in Spain by Just Colour Graphic S. L.

This book is printed on paper from certified and well-managed sources.

ACKNOWLEDGEMENTS

*The publisher would like to thank the following for the permission to reproduce
photographs*: MorgueFile p.47 (radio); Oxford University Press
pp.4 (Buckingham Palace/Corel), 4 (Edinburgh/Photodisc), 4 (Cardiff
Castle/Photodisc), 6 (Australian flag/EyeWire), 6 (Canadian flag/EyeWire),
6 (Indian flag/EyeWire), 6 (New Zealand flag/EyeWire), 6 (United Kingdom
flag/EyeWire), 6 (flags/Photodisc), 7 (globe/Photodisc), 7 (Statue of Liberty/
Photodisc), 7 (White House/Photodisc), 8 (teenager with laptop/Comstock),
8 (girl texting/Photodisc), 9 (kids playing/Photodisc), 9 (man on computer/
Photodisc), 10 (bride and bridesmaids/Digital Vision), 10 (bank card/Digital
Vision), 10 (motorcyclist/Joe Fox Motorsport), 12 (flip phone/Photodisc),
12 (traffic/Photodisc), 12 (beer/Stockbyte), 12 (wine/Stockbyte), 12 (pills/
Corbis/Digital Stock), 13 (congestion/Digital Vision), 14 (girls/), 16 (classroom/
Corbis/Digital Stock), 17 (students/Corbis), 18 (dinner table/Photodisc),
18 (Halloween/Creatas), 18 (pumpkin/Digital Vision), 18 (fireworks/
Corel), 18 (fire/Photodisc), 20 (ladder/Photodisc), 20 (cat/Index Stock),
20 (rabbits/Photodisc), 21 (Tower of London/Photodisc), 21 (Beefeater/
Corel), 22 (fast food/Chris King), 22 (paperboy/Chris King), 22 (walking dog/
Brand X Pictures), 24 (Oxford/Digital Vision), 25 (diver/Photodisc), 25 (fish/
Stockbyte), 26 (abseiling/Photodisc), 26 (paraglider/Photodisc), 26 (surfing/
Corel), 26 (canoeist/Photodisc), 26 (rugby/Photodisc), 26 (basketball/Brand
X Pictures), 28 (teen girls/Chris King), 29 (listening to music/Stockbyte),
30 (London/Photodisc), 31 (shopping centre/Photodisc), 33 (underground/
Image Source), 34 (Colosseum/Photodisc), 34 (Pyramid of Kukulkan/Corbis/
Digital Stock), 34 (Taj Mahal/Photodisc), 34 (Monastery at Petra/Photodisc),
34 (Machu Picchu/Photodisc), 34 (Rio de Janeiro/Photodisc), 35 (Great Wall
of China/Photodisc), 35 (Egypt/Corbis/Digital Stock), 36 (Tate Modern/John
Foxx), 36 (Tate Modern/Image Source), 37 (Angel of the North/Digital Vision),
38 (airport/Digital Vision), 38 (forest/Photodisc), 39 (Alpine pass/Photodisc),
39 (leaf/imagebroker), 41 (wedding/Photodisc), 42 (sheep/Photodisc),
43 (weaver/Photodisc), 44 (beach/Photodisc), 45 (Snowdonia/Rob Rayworth),
45 (Loch Lomond/Photodisc), 45 (river/Corel), 46 (Marconi/Illustrated London
News), 47 (phonograph advert/Illustrated London News), 47 (light bulb/
Photodisc), 48 (food pyramid/Photodisc), 49 (canteen/Chris King), 49 (lunch
tray/Photodisc), 50 (compacter at landfill/Photodisc), 50 (gift/Photodisc),
50 (paper/Digital Vision), 50 (recycling bins/Photodisc), 50 (recycling glass/
Photodisc), 52 (station/Dominic Burke), 53 (street/Photodisc), 54 (Euro coin/
Sam Toren), 54 (European flag/Brand X Pictures), 54 (European Parliament,
Brussels/Image Source); Stock Xchng pp.25 (Indian school), 28 (band), 31 (Fifth
Avenue), 32 (underground sign, blitz), 38 (aeroplane), 42 (loom), 43 (thread),
51 (chewing gum), 52 (railway station), 56 (candle), 57 (Auschwitz); University
of Texas Libraries pp.40 (Jane Austen), 46 (Thomas Edison); Wikimedia
Commons pp.4 (Stormont), 24 (Harvard), 55 (European Parliament), 56 (Jews).

Cover images by: Photodisc

Illustrations by: Peter Bull pp.71 (Map United Kingdom), 72 (Map USA and Canada)

Contents

Culture

CLIL

1 READING & SPEAKING

a In pairs, ask and answer the questions.

● What is the capital city of your country?

● Have you visited it?

● What are its famous monuments?

b Read the following text quickly. Put the capital cities in order according to their populations from largest to smallest.

Cardiff   Belfast   London   Edinburgh

The United Kingdom

The United Kingdom (UK) is made up of four countries: England, Scotland, Wales, and Northern Ireland. The four capitals of the United Kingdom's constituent countries are London (England), Edinburgh (Scotland), Cardiff (Wales), and Belfast (Northern Ireland). London is also the capital of the UK.

London

London is the capital city of England and the UK. It is in the south east of England, and is on the river Thames. It has a population of approximately 8 million people. London has many famous monuments such as the Tower of London, Big Ben, Buckingham Palace, and the London Eye. It also has well-known museums and galleries such as the British Museum, the National Gallery, and Tate Modern. The

Buckingham Palace

West End, with locations like Oxford Street, Leicester Square, Covent Garden, and Piccadilly Circus is London's entertainment and shopping district. London's tallest building is One Canada Square in Canary Wharf. It has 52 floors! For a big city, London has many green spaces, for example Hyde, St James', and Greenwich parks. The Houses of Parliament, in Westminster, is the home of the Government of the UK.

Edinburgh

Edinburgh is the capital of Scotland and its second largest city after Glasgow. Edinburgh is in south-east Scotland, on the south shore of the Firth of Forth, on the North Sea. It is the seat of the Scottish Parliament. Edinburgh has a total population of around 450,000. In August, during the Edinburgh festival, its population doubles! Its main attractions include Edinburgh Castle which is at the top of an extinct volcano, and the Royal Mile – the historical street which leads down from the Castle. Visitors should also take in Holyrood House, St Giles Cathedral, Princes Street for shopping, and the magnificent Forth Rail Bridge on the Firth of Forth. Edinburgh's most famous park is Princes Street Gardens.

Belfast

Belfast is the capital of Northern Ireland and its largest city. It has a population of approximately 280,000 people. Belfast is on Northern Ireland's east coast, at the mouth of the River Lagan. Many parts of the city centre are being redeveloped. New developments include Victoria Square, the Cathedral Quarter and the regeneration of the Titanic Quarter (the ocean liner

Stormont

Titanic was built in Belfast). Belfast has over forty public parks. One of the most popular is the Botanic Gardens. The Northern Ireland Assembly is in Belfast, at Stormont.

Cardiff

Cardiff, on the country's south coast, is the capital city of Wales. The river Taff flows through this city with a population of approximately 321,000 people. Cardiff has many beautiful places of interest, and is one of the top ten cities to visit according to the British Tourist Authority. One of the cities oldest monuments is Cardiff Castle. Other places to visit are the Wales Millennium Centre, home to the Welsh National Opera, the Millennium Sports stadium, and the National Museum and Gallery. Cardiff's town centre is very green – its most famous parks are Roath park, Cathays park and Bute park. Cardiff is also one of the best places for shopping in the UK!

Edinburgh

Cardiff Castle

c   Read the text again. In pairs, complete the chart.

City	Country	Population	Places of interest to visit	Parks	Rivers
1 London					
2 Edinburgh					
3 Belfast					
4 Cardiff					

d   In pairs, complete the sentences with London, Edinburgh, Cardiff, or Belfast.

1 _____ is the city where the Titanic was built.

2 _____ is one of the best cities for shopping in the UK.

3 _____ has a skyscraper with 52 floors.

4 _____ has a castle which is built on an extinct volcano.

2 LISTENING & SPEAKING

a   **1.1** Listen to Chiara talking about her favourite place in London. Answer the questions.

1 How often does Chiara go to London?

2 Where is her favourite place in London?

3 What is a busker?

4 What does she like doing at her favourite place?

5 What does Chiara like best about her favourite place?

What do you think?

☀ Which is the best city in your country? Why?

PROJECT

Write an email (100 words) to a friend about the capital city of your country. Include information on:
• where the city is
• which river flows through it
• its population
• what its famous monuments and museums are
• what young people can do there

1 SPEAKING

a In pairs, answer the questions.

ENGLISH AROUND THE WORLD QUIZ

1 Approximately how many people speak English as their native language?

a 150 million **b** 295 million **c** 380 million

2 Tick (✓) the countries where English is an official language:

a ___ New Zealand **f** ___ Canada

b ___ India **g** ___ Australia

c ___ The Bahamas **h** ___ South Africa

d ___ Jamaica **i** ___ United States of America

e ___ Philippines

3 Match these English words with the language of their origin.

a mosquito **1** French

b shampoo **2** Italian

c generous **3** Norwegian

d piano **4** Hindi

e ski **5** Spanish

4 Match these British English words with their American English equivalents.

a ___ flat **1** highway

b ___ pavement **2** drapes

c ___ rubbish **3** apartment

d ___ curtains **4** sidewalk

e ___ motorway **5** trash

5 Change the spelling of these words from American English to British English.

a color **1** _____

b center **2** _____

c TV program **3** _____

d gray **4** _____

e favorite **5** _____

2 READING

a Complete the text by putting the verbs in the correct form.

use study spread be speak

Did you know...?

Over 380 million people [1]_____ English as a first language, in countries such as the UK, the USA, Australia, Canada, New Zealand, and Ireland. It is also a second, and official, language throughout the world, including India, Pakistan, South Africa, and the Philippines.

However, English [2]_____ the most commonly spoken native language in the world. It is in third place behind Mandarin Chinese and Spanish.

The areas of science, business, aviation, entertainment, technology, and diplomacy all [3]_____ English as the main language of communication.

English [4]_____ around the world, due to the influence of the British Empire and the importance of the United States, economically and culturally, after World War II.

More people [5]_____ English as a foreign language in the European Union than any other. Then comes French followed by German and Spanish.

b 🔊 **2.1** Listen and check.

c Match the highlighted words or phrases with a definition.

1 accepted and approved by the government

2 connected with the place where you were born or where you have always lived

3 the power to affect, change or control something or somebody

4 managing relations between different countries

5 the designing, building and flying of aircraft

d Read the article again and mark the sentence T (true), F (false), or DS (doesn't say). Correct the false sentences.

1 English is an official language in the UK.

2 More people speak Spanish as a native language than English.

3 Airline pilots must be able to speak and understand English.

4 The influence of the United States after the war helped to spread English worldwide.

5 More people study German than French in the European Union.

3 LISTENING & SPEAKING

a 2.2 In pairs, listen and match the sentence halves.

a The United States is the country with

b English speaking settlers arrived

c Noah Webster was

d In 1828 Webster

1 in North America in the 17th Century.

2 wrote *An American Dictionary of the English Language.*

3 the highest population of native English speakers.

4 a popular American author.

b 2.2 Listen again and mark the sentences T (true) or F (false). Correct the false sentences.

1 The English language spread around the world because of the British Empire.

2 British and American English have the same grammar and vocabulary.

3 Noah Webster wrote his Dictionary to illustrate the similarities between American and British English.

4 Webster simplified American English spellings.

5 American spelling today is exactly the same as in Webster's dictionary.

What do you think?

✺ English is one of the most widely spoken languages in the world. How do you think it will be important for your future?

PROJECT

Find out about your language, using the Internet. Write an article (100 words) for a school magazine. Include information on:

• how many people speak the language

• in which countries people speak the language

• any dialects or different versions of the language

• how these dialects or different versions began

1 LISTENING & SPEAKING

a In pairs, ask and answer the questions.

- How much free time do you have each week?
- Which of the following do you do in your free time?

listen to music   chat online with friends   watch TV
send text messages   go shopping   do sport

b **3.1** Listen to two British teenagers talking about what they do in their free time. Who does the most sport, Will or Emily?

c **3.1** Listen again and mark the sentences T (true) or F (false). Correct the false sentences.

1 Will plays football at the weekends.
2 Will doesn't watch a lot of TV.
3 Will and his friends usually go to the cinema.
4 Emily uses the Internet every day.
5 Emily reads a lot of books.
6 Emily's mum would like her to get more exercise.

d Ask and answer with a partner.

1 How much do you use the Internet?
2 How many text messages do you send a day?
3 How often do you listen to music?
4 How much TV do you watch a day?
5 Do you go usually to the cinema or watch DVDs?
6 Do you play any sports in your free time?

e Look at the pie chart showing how Will spends his free time each week. Would you like to spend your free time in a similar way? Why (not)?

- Playing football
- Playing computer games
- Watching TV/DVDs
- Listening to music
- Reading

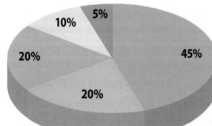

Are computers bad for your health?

Many people are worried that teenagers today
¹_____ getting enough exercise in their free
time. The popularity of computers, mobile phones
and modern technology means young people are
²_____ less time doing activities like sport and
more time looking at computer screens and mobile
keypads. Lack of exercise leads to health problems
later in life. A recent survey in the UK showed
that some teenagers are ³_____ the Internet
for 16 hours or more per week. In China, the
Government ⁴_____ so worried about teenagers
becoming addicted to the Internet that it is
⁵_____ of restricting the number of hours that
they can spend online, and encouraging them to
do more sport in their free time.

Health problems aren't the only issue. Thanks to
computers, teenagers are spending less time with
their friends and more time on their own. When
teenagers ⁶_____ the Internet, send emails
and text a lot, they are ⁷_____ themselves
and they aren't ⁸_____ how to socialize and
behave in society properly. However, some people
argue that the Internet offers its own form of
social interaction: young people can chat, talk
about their likes and dislikes, music tastes, what's
bothering them, and communicate with each other
on line. In fact, the Internet can actually help
teenagers build and maintain friendships. The
survey concluded that the Internet is a positive
thing but it is important to use it with caution
and in moderation!

2 READING & SPEAKING

a Read the text about teenagers and their free time and complete it with the words in the box.

using   aren't   spending   is   thinking
isolating   learning   use

b Read the text again. In pairs, answer the questions.
1 According to the text, why are teenagers doing less exercise in their free time?
2 Why is it important to exercise?
3 How may hours a week do some people use the Internet?
4 What does the Chinese Government want to do?
5 Why are some teenagers spending less time with their friends?
6 How can the Internet help young people to socialise?

c Match the highlighted words with the correct definitions.
1 communicating with someone
2 unable to stop doing something
3 stopping or limiting someone
4 the buttons on a phone
5 a reasonable amount
6 carefulness

What do you think?
❋ Do young people in your country get enough exercise? Why (not)?
❋ How often do you use computers? What for?
❋ Do you think the Government should control how people use computers at home? Why (not)?

PROJECT
Conduct a survey in your class. Find out how people spend their free time. Look at the results and draw a pie chart. Write a short report (100 words). Include information on:
• the most popular activities
• the least popular activities
• any interesting or unusual activities

1 LISTENING & SPEAKING

a In pairs, answer the questions about age limits in the UK.
Circle a, b, or c. Compare with another pair.

How old do you have to be...

1 to vote?
   a 16   **b** 18   **c** 21

2 to buy alcohol?
   a 16   **b** 18   **c** 21

3 to buy cigarettes?
   a 14   **b** 16   **c** 18

4 to drive a motorbike up to 50cc?
   a 14   **b** 16   **c** 17

5 before you can get married?
   a 16   **b** 18   **c** 20

6 before you can leave school?
   a 14   **b** 16   **c** 18

7 to buy a National Lottery ticket?
   a 14   **b** 16   **c** 17

8 to get a tattoo?
   a 14   **b** 16   **c** 18

9 to have a bank account?
   a from birth   **b** 5   **c** 10

b **4.1** Listen and check.

2 READING & SPEAKING

a Read the article and complete it with the words from below.

politics   jobs   cars   home
party   debate   army   decisions

There is a big **1**_____ in the UK at the moment, about whether or not to lower the voting age to 16. Those in favour of lowering it argue that it is unfair that you can join the **2**_____ at that age but not choose your Prime Minister. They say that many 16 year olds have **3**_____ and pay taxes and so they should be allowed to vote for the political **4**_____ that best represents their needs. However, those in favour of keeping the voting age at 18 argue that many 16-year-olds don't know enough about politics to make informed **5**_____ about who to vote for. A lot of 16-year-olds still go to school and live at **6**_____ with their parents. They don't all pay taxes, they can't drive **7**_____ and they usually don't own houses, so most Government's policies don't affect them. Many 16-year-olds are not interested in voting anyway and often find **8**_____ boring. They wouldn't know who to vote for so therefore it's best to keep the age limit at 18.

TO VOTE OR NOT TO VOTE X

b Work in pairs, **A** and **B**. **A** make a list of arguments for lowering the voting age, **B** make a list of arguments for not changing the voting age. Add your own ideas.

A Why the voting age should be 16	B Why the voting age should be 18

c Share your ideas and complete the table.

3 SPEAKING

a Imagine you can vote. What issues are important to you? Choose your three most important issues from the list below.
1 Cheaper trains and buses ___
2 Global warming and recycling ___
3 Better health care ___
4 Drugs and crime ___
5 Bullying ___
6 Vandalism ___
7 Stopping terrorism ___
8 Animal rights ___

b In groups, compare opinions. Which issue does your group think is the most important?

c Write some notes and prepare a presentation. Include information on:
● your group's most important issue.
● your reasons for choosing it.
● solutions to the problem.

What do you think?

✳ In the UK, you can join the army at 16 but only vote when you are 18. Is this the same in your country? Do you think this is right? Why (not)?
✳ What age do you think young people should be able to vote?

PROJECT

Write a paragraph (100 words) describing the different age limits in your country. Include information on:
When you can...
• vote
• buy alcohol/cigarettes
• drive a motorbike/car
• leave school
• get married
...and whether you think these are the right age limits or not.

1 READING & LISTENING

a In pairs, ask and answer the questions.

- Are the roads in your country safe? Why (not)?
- Look at the photos below. Why do you think these things can be dangerous to road users? Give reasons for your answer.

Road safety

The 27th April is European Road Safety Day for young road users. It's aim is to educate young road users to [1]_____ road safety, and to reduce by 50 percent the number of road accidents in Europe within two years. Road accidents are the main cause of death in Europe [2]_____ between the ages of 10 and 24. On 27th April, many schools in Europe organize special events, for example discussions, workshops, and poster exhibitions to promote a road safety culture.

Each year 40,000 people die on the roads in Europe in road accidents. One third of fatal accidents are caused by drivers [3]_____.
Other causes of accidents are drinking and driving, or driving under the effect of drugs or medicine; drivers and passengers [4]_____ or moped riders not wearing a crash helmet, and road users not respecting [5]_____.

b Read the article and put phrases A–E in the correct places.

A road signs or markings
B for young people
C driving too fast
D think more about
E not wearing seat belts

c **5.1** Listen and check your answers.

DVD 3 Learning to drive

2 READING & SPEAKING

a Read the article. In pairs, answer the questions.

What three things must you not do if you are driving?

What do you think the title means?

ZERO
LIMIT IS THE SAFEST LIMIT!

Alcohol affects your ability to drive safely. You may feel fine but you are not. Drinking alcohol seriously affects your driving. It can slow down your reactions or overstimulate you and cause you to take risks. Even if you drink one glass of wine, a can, or a bottle of beer you are 30–40% less reactive than someone who has not drunk anything. Also, alcohol can make you sleepy, and reduce your concentration. Each year around 3000 people in the UK are killed or seriously injured in car crashes where drivers have been drinking. The only safe option is a 'zero limit' option which means do not drink any alcohol if you plan to drive, and never offer an alcoholic drink to anyone else who is driving.

Drugs can also affect the way you drive; slowing reactions, coordination, and sometimes making you sleepy or likely to take risks. It is not safe to be a passenger in a car if the driver has been drinking alcohol or taken drugs.

Another danger is mobile phone use. Speaking on the phone is a distraction, and driving at the same time can cause accidents. They are also dangerous for other road users. Sometimes accidents happen because of a pedestrian sending a text message, or speaking on a mobile phone, while crossing the road. The safest option is to turn off your mobile phone when driving and never use your phone when crossing or waiting to cross a road. Remember, it is not safe to be a passenger in a car if the driver is using a mobile phone without a hands-free set.

b Read the article again and answer the questions.

1 What are the effects on you if you have drunk alcohol and drive?

2 What is a safe amount of alcohol to drink if you are driving?

3 How can drugs effect your driving?

4 Why are mobile phones dangerous when you are driving?

5 Why are mobile phones dangerous if you are a pedestrian?

c In pairs, <u>underline</u> any words or phrases you don't know. Try to guess their meaning. Then check them in your dictionary. Choose five to learn.

What do you think?

✳ What do you think young people should do to improve their road safety?

PROJECT

You are going to organize a special event for European Road Safety Day in your school next year. Design a poster for the day and plan an activity for your class. Include information on:
• what the Road Safety Day is
• when it is
• what the aims are
• what event your school is organizing
• what time the event starts
• how students can participate

1 READING & VOCABULARY

a Ask and answer the questions in pairs.

- Do you know anyone that has been bullied? What happened?
- Have you every been bullied? When? What happened?

b Read the text and match the highlighted words with their definitions.

1 to respect yourself
2 a piece of news about someone that might not be true
3 to behave unfairly or in a cruel way towards someone
4 belief that somebody / something is good, honest, or sincere
5 something that happens
6 being sure about your own abilities

The end of the road for bullies?

1_____

Bullying is when a person is picked on by an individual or group of people. It can involve hitting, threatening or intimidating someone, spreading rumours, or encouraging others to reject or exclude someone. Cyber-bullies send people nasty texts, emails or write horrible things about the person they are bullying on Internet blogs. Almost 30 percent of teenagers in the United States have been involved in bullying as either a bully or a target of bullying or both. Bullying can make you feel anxious and afraid. It can affect your concentration in school and can make you want to avoid school in some cases. It also affects your self-esteem. However, many successful adults were bullied when they were young for example David Beckham and Tom Cruise!

2_____

You can talk to your parents or an adult that you trust. You can also tell a friend what is happening and ask him / her to help you. If the bullying happens at school you can tell a teacher or your headmaster / mistress.

3_____

You should not show that you are angry or upset. Bullies want to get a reaction. If you are calm, and hide your emotions, they may stop. Ignore hurtful emails or texts and you will show that you do not care. It's best not to fight back. Often bullies are very strong and you may make the situation worse. It is a good idea to try and avoid being alone in the places where you know the bully is likely to pick on you. This might mean changing the way you go to school or avoiding parts of the school. Keep a diary about what is happening. Write down details of the incidents and how you feel.

4_____

Bullying can affect how you feel about yourself. Sometimes you feel alone if you are bullied, so it is important to make new friendships with people who share your interests. You could join a sports club outside of school or participate in extra-curricular activities. Be confident.

It is not all good news for Bullies! Many schools in the United Kingdom and United States of America are introducing programmes to reduce bullying and also to enforce rules against bullying.

c Read the text again and put the headings in the correct place.

How can I feel better about myself?

What should you do if you are being bullied?

Who should you tell if you are being bullied?

What is bullying?

d Read the article again and match the sentence halves.

1 Ignore hurtful emails and texts

2 You should not show

3 You can talk to

4 Keep a diary about

a that you are angry or upset.

b a parent or an adult you trust.

c and you will show that you do not care.

d what is happening.

2 LISTENING & SPEAKING

a 6.1 Listen to Anthea talk about being bullied at school. Mark the sentences T (true) or F (false), correct the false sentences.

1 Anthea was bullied at primary school.

2 The bully was called Michael.

3 Anthea's nickname was 'cow'.

4 She got her nickname because she had a double chin.

5 Bullying made Anthea feel physically sick.

6 When she left school she became a journalist.

b 6.1 Listen again and complete the sentences.

1 I will never forget my _____

_____ .

2 My _____ was 'goat'.

3 I had terrible _____ stomach.

4 My name was no longer Anthea _____ .

5 Sticks and stones _____ .

6 _____ never hurt me.

What do you think?

※ Do you think you should tell your teacher if you are being bullied. Why (not)?

PROJECT

Write a short article (100 words) about cyber-bullying. Use the Internet or magazines to help you.

Include information on:

• what cyber-bullying is

• what cyber-bullies do

• how you can protect yourself from a cyber-bully

1 READING & VOCABULARY

a In pairs, ask and answer the questions.

- Do you like school? Why (not)?
- What is your favourite subject? Why?

b Look at the table showing the different school systems in the United Kingdom and the United States. Complete the chart with information about your country.

School System in the United Kingdom	School System in the United States of America	My Country
age 3–5 Nursery School	age 5–6 Kindergarten	
age 5–11 Primary School	age 6–11 Elementary School	
age 11–16 Secondary School	age 11–14 Junior High School	
16–18 Secondary School – sixth form	age 14–18 Senior High School	

c Read the text and match the highlighted words with their definitions.

1 a programme of study for schools.
2 the final two years of secondary school
3 something that must be done
4 to move on

d In pairs, cover the text and answer the questions from memory.

1 What are the ages of compulsory education in the UK?
2 What is a grammar school?
3 When do students take GCSE exams? How many do they take?
4 What school subjects do students study in the first three years of secondary school?
5 What is streaming?

Education in the United Kingdom

In the United Kingdom it is compulsory to go to school between the ages of five and sixteen, which means students have to go to primary school and then secondary school. There are different types of secondary school, such as Grammar Schools or Academies. Some secondary schools are private. These are called Independent Schools or Public Schools. Schools in England, Wales, and Northern Ireland follow the National Curriculum, which means that all schools follow the same syllabus. Scotland has its own Curriculum. In the UK, students automatically progress to the next level of year, and do not repeat the year even if they fail the end of year exams. In the first three years of secondary education students study English, Maths, Science, Design and Technology, Information and Communication Technology (ICT), History, Geography, Modern Foreign languages, Music, Physical Education, Citizenship and Religious Education. Then they choose between eight and ten subjects to study for GCSE (General Certificate of Secondary Education) exams when they are 16. After two years in the sixth form they take an average of 3 A-level (Advanced Level) examinations. Some schools, especially for subjects such as Maths, English, and Modern Languages, divide pupils according to ability into groups, for example A, B, C, D. This is called streaming.

DVD 7 An American in Britain

2 READING & SPEAKING

a Read the article about schools in the United States of America. Put phrases A–D in the correct places.

A you can choose to do

B with Elementary School

C students go to Junior High School

D compulsory education

Education in the USA

In the USA [1]_____ begins at the age of six [2]_____ and then depending on the state, children can leave at the age of 16 or 18. Between the ages of 11 and 14 [3]_____ and then at 14 they go to Senior High School where in grade 12 (the final year of High School) they get their High School Diploma. Students study Science, Mathematics, English, Social Science, and Physical Education as well as other subjects called 'electives'. These are subjects [4]_____ for example Visual Arts, Technology, Foreign Languages, Computer Science, and Drama.

3 LISTENING & SPEAKING

a In pairs, ask and answer the question.

Would you like to wear a school uniform? Why (not)?

b **7.1** In Britain students wear a school uniform. Listen to three students talking about their school uniforms. Complete the chart.

	Jumper/cardigan	Skirt/trousers	Blouse/shirt	Tie	Shoes	Socks	Likes / does not like school uniform?
Robert						grey	
Sofia							
Anthea				burgundy and yellow			

What do you think?

✳ In some schools in the UK, especially for subjects such as Maths, English, and Modern Languages, schools stream pupils on ability. Do you think this is a good idea? Why (not)?

✳ What are the advantages and disadvantages? Give reasons for your answers.

PROJECT

Write an email (100 words) to a penfriend telling him or her about your school and your school day.

Include information on:
• where your school is
• school hours
• what year you are in
• where you have lunch
• what subjects you study

1 LISTENING & SPEAKING

a What do you know about these festivals and celebrations? In pairs, ask and answer the questions.

1 Where do people celebrate Thanksgiving?

2 When do people celebrate Thanksgiving?

3 What is Hogmanay?

4 Where is it celebrated?

5 Who was Guy Fawkes?

6 When do people celebrate Bonfire Night?

7 Was Halloween originally an American festival?

8 Where does the name 'Halloween' come from?

b **8.1** In pairs, listen and check your answers.

2 READING

a Read the texts and put the phrases A–H in the correct places.

A with fireworks and a big bonfire

B sing Auld Lang Syne

C tradition of bobbing for apples

D gifts of coal and whisky

E ghosts of the dead

F discovered the plot

G in a ship called the Mayflower

H became a National Holiday in America in 1863

b Read the texts again and mark the sentences T (true) or F (false). Correct the false ones.

1 The first Canadian Thanksgiving was in 1620.

2 First footing is the Scottish tradition of the first person to enter a house before midnight.

3 The Hogmanay celebrations in Edinburgh last for four days.

4 Guy Fawkes planned to blow up the Houses of Parliament by himself.

5 The Celts celebrated their New Year on the 31st October.

6 The Irish brought Halloween to America in the 20th Century.

THANKSGIVING

People in the USA and Canada celebrate Thanksgiving every year. In the USA, Thanksgiving is on the fourth Thursday of November. The festival marks the end of the harvest season and people usually eat turkey and pumpkin pie. In 1620, a group of people called the Pilgrims arrived in America [1]_____. They were originally from England, but left as they didn't agree with the church's ideas. Their first winter in America was devastating and more than half of them died. But the next year they had a good harvest and celebrated with a feast giving thanks – together with the Indians who helped them survive. Thanksgiving [2]_____, when President Lincoln decided the last Thursday in November would be a national day of Thanksgiving.

In Canada, Thanksgiving is on the second Monday in October and it is usually a three or four day weekend festival. The history of Thanksgiving in Canada goes back to an English explorer, Martin Frobisher, who established a settlement in Canada. In 1578, he celebrated his survival of the long and dangerous journey from England to North America with a formal ceremony. This was the first Canadian Thanksgiving.

HOGMANAY

Hogmanay is the name given to the celebration of the New Year in Scotland. The tradition of First footing is associated with this. This involves being the first person to enter a house immediately after midnight, usually carrying [3]_____ to bring good

3 LISTENING

a **8.2** Listen to Sam talking about how he celebrates Christmas. Where does he go on Christmas Day?

b **8.2** Listen again and answer the questions.

1 Where is Sam from?

2 What is the weather like in Australia at Christmas?

3 What is the Carols by Candlelight Festival?

4 When does Sam open his Christmas presents.

5 Does Sam like Christmas?

luck. A tall, dark, handsome man is supposed to bring the most luck! Some people think this is because in the past, a man with dark hair was welcome as people presumed he was Scottish; a blond or red-haired man could have been an unwelcome Viking. At midnight, people [4]_____, a traditional poem reinterpreted by the Scottish poet Robert Burns. This is now sung in many countries.

Edinburgh holds one of the biggest and most famous Hogmanay celebrations. There is a big street party and the celebrations usually last for four days, from 29th December to the 1st January.

BONFIRE NIGHT

In 1605, there was a plot to blow up the Houses of Parliament in London. Thirteen Catholic men, including Guy Fawkes, planned to kill the Protestant King James I and all the English politicians. They thought the King was persecuting their religion. They put thirty-six barrels of gunpowder in a cellar under the Parliament. However, the King [5]_____ and sent his men to stop them. On the 5th November, 1605, they caught Guy Fawkes in the cellar with the gunpowder. They tortured and executed him. After this, people lit bonfires to celebrate the safety of the King.

The 5th November is called Bonfire Night and it is celebrated every year by people in England [6]_____. Children make a puppet called a 'Guy' to burn on the bonfire. Even today, when the Queen enters Parliament for the State Opening of Parliament, it is traditional to search the cellars before she enters.

HALLOWEEN

Halloween is celebrated on the 31st October. Many people think it is an America tradition, but the origins of

Halloween are much older. It was originally a Celtic festival called Samhain. The Celts celebrated their New Year on the 1st November, which marked the end of the summer and the beginning of the winter. They believed that the night before the New Year, the boundary between the worlds of the living and the dead became blurred and the [7]_____ returned to earth. The Romans conquered the Celts and spread Christianity throughout their lands. Samhain became part of other Roman traditions that took place in October, such as their day to honour Pomona, the Roman goddess of fruit and trees. The symbol of Pomona is the apple, which might explain the origin of the [8]_____ on Halloween.

It was a Christian tradition to dedicate a day to remembering saints and martyrs and in AD 609, Pope Boniface IV designated 13th May as this day. In AD 837, Pope Gregory IV changed the date to the 1st November. This was called All Saints' Day or All Hallows' Day. The night before was All Hallows' Eve (Halloween). Irish immigrants bought the custom of Halloween to America in the 1840s. Today, people in many countries celebrate and go to Halloween parties and children go from house to house knocking on doors chanting 'Trick or Treat' and people either give them some sweets to eat or the children play a trick on them.

What do you think?
* Which is your favourite festival in your country?
* How do you celebrate it?

PROJECT

Write a paragraph (100 words) describing the most popular festival in your country. Include information on:
• when it is
• what its origins are
• how you are going to celebrate it this year

superstition /ˌsuːpəˈstɪʃn; ˌsjuː-/ *noun* [C,U] a belief that cannot be explained by reason or science: *According to superstition, it's unlucky to walk under a ladder.* ▶ **superstitious** /ˌsuːpə-ˈstɪʃəs; ˌsjuː-/ *adj*: *I never do anything important on Friday 13th – I'm superstitious.*

(from *Oxford Students' Dictionary*)

1 LISTENING & SPEAKING

a In pairs, ask and answer the questions.

- Are you superstitious? Why (not)?
- Do you know anyone who is?
- What superstitions do they have?

b Look at the pictures. In pairs, ask and answer the questions.

1 Do any of these things bring good or bad luck in your country?

2 Do any of the things stop bad luck?

c (9.1) Listen to three teenagers talking about superstitions in their country. Fill the chart with the information.

Things that bring good luck	Things that bring bad luck	Things that stop bad luck

d (9.1) Listen again and mark the sentences T (true) or F (false). Correct the false ones.

1 If you break a mirror in England it brings seven years of good luck.

2 A white rabbit brings bad luck in England.

3 The number thirteen is a lucky number in America.

4 If you spill salt, to stop the bad luck you must throw some over your left shoulder.

5 Black cats are unlucky in the USA.

6 Brides in England wear something pink on their wedding day.

2 READING & SPEAKING

a Read the article and match the highlighted words with their definition.

1 dangerous or cruel

2 a black bird that looks like a crow

3 to cut off feathers

4 a guard at the Tower of London

5 the person who keeps ravens

6 a place to live and to sleep

7 baby birds

b Cover the text. In pairs, answer the questions from memory.

1 What will happen if the ravens leave the Tower of London?

2 How many ravens must be kept there?

3 Who do historians think started this legend?

4 How do they stop the ravens from flying away?

5 Who looks after the ravens?

The RAVENS in the TOWER of LONDON

In some parts of the world the raven is considered a bad omen and a symbol of the supernatural, but in the UK the raven is very important indeed. A legend connected to the Tower of London says that six ravens must live there. If the ravens fly away the great white Tower will fall down and there will be a terrible disaster in England. This legend is so established that the British government pays for six ravens to be kept at the Tower of London. To stop the birds flying away one of their wings is clipped – a simple operation that does not hurt the raven.

Historians think that King Charles II (1630–1685) was the monarch who first declared that the birds should be kept at the Tower to prevent disaster. The ravens even have Raven's Lodgings, and a Beefeater has the job of Raven Master at the Tower, taking care of their feeding and well-being. Ravens can be quite vicious birds and they only respond to the Raven Master. He builds a relationship with the ravens as he takes the fledglings into his home and hand cares for them for six weeks. Thousands of visitors from all over the world visit the ravens at the Tower of London every day.

What do you think?

* Which superstitions do you have in your country?
* Do you think people should believe in superstitions? Why (not)?

PROJECT

Many superstitions have ancient origins. Choose a superstition that some people believe in your country. Find out more about it. Use the Internet to help you. Write a short presentation (100 words). Include information on:
• what the superstition is
• what its origins are
• if it brings good luck or bad luck

1 READING & SPEAKING

a In pairs, ask and answer the questions.

- How old do you have to be to get a job in your country?
- Do you or your friends have a part time job? If so, how many hours do you work a week?

b Read the Frequently Asked Questions (FAQ) about teenagers and work in the UK. Match the questions A–H with the correct answers 1–7.

A When can children work?

B What kinds of part time jobs can teenagers do?

C How many hours can 13 and 14 year olds work?

D How much money do teenagers get paid for working?

E How old do children have to be before they can work?

F What about working during the school holidays?

G What do teenagers need to start working?

H Are the rules different for older teenagers?

c Read the FAQ again. Talk to a partner.

1 Are the rules the same in your country?

2 What kinds of part-time jobs can teenagers do in your country?

3 Are they the same as in the UK?

FAQ about teenagers

1 In the UK, children are not legally allowed to work until they are 13.

2 Children can only work after 7 a.m. and before 7 p.m. On a school day they can only work for up to 2 hours.

3 If it's a school day, 13 and 14-year-olds can work up to 2 hours in one day, either between 7 a.m. to the start of school or from when the school closes to 7 p.m. On Saturdays they can work up to 5 hours between 7 a.m. and 7 p.m. and on Sundays up to 2 hours between 7 a.m. and 11 a.m.

DVD 5 **Working with animals**

2 LISTENING

a 🔘 **10.1** Listen to three teenagers talking about their part time jobs. Complete the chart.

Person	Job	Like?
1 Jessica		yes/no
2 Alex		yes/no
3 Isabel		yes/no

b 🔘 **10.1** Listen again and answer the questions.

1 How many hours a week does Jessica work?
2 How much does Jessica get paid?
3 Does Alex work at the weekend?
4 What time does Alex start work?
5 What hours does Isabel work on Saturdays?
6 How much does she get paid?

c In pairs, ask and answer the questions.

1 Which of these 3 part time jobs would you like to do and why?
2 What would be your ideal part time job?

What do you think?

 In the UK, workers under 16 often don't get paid the National Minimum Wage. Is this fair? Why (not)?

 Many people believe teenagers should concentrate on studying instead of having part-time jobs. Do you agree? Why (not)?

PROJECT

Write a short description (100 words) of your ideal part time job for a school magazine. Include information on:
• what you do
• how many hours you work
• how much you get paid

and part-time work in the UK

4 During term time, 13 and 14-year-olds can work up to a maximum of 12 hours a week (Including weekends) but during the school holidays (including weekends) they can work up to a maximum of 25 hours week: 5 hours a day, between 7 a.m.–7 p.m. on any day except Sunday when they can only do 2 hours between 7 a.m.–7 p.m.

5 Yes, they are. 15 and 16-year-olds can work for up to 8 hours on Saturdays and up to a maximum of 35 hours per week during school holidays.

6 They need to have a work permit. An application form for the work permit can be obtained from school or local Education Welfare Office.

7 It depends on the kind of work, but could be anything up to around £4 per hour. There is a National Minimum Wage in the UK but this doesn't apply to workers under 16.

8 The most popular is probably delivering newspapers to houses before they go to school. They can also baby-sit, work in shops or hairdressers, work in a riding stable, or in a café or restaurant.

11 University and gap years

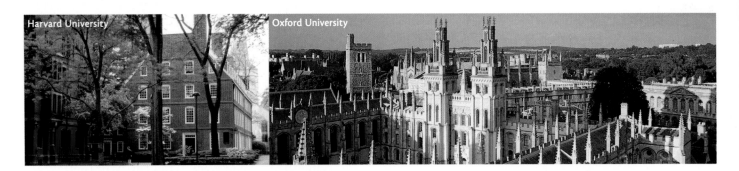

Harvard University   Oxford University

1 LISTENING

a In pairs, answer the questions.

- Can you name any famous universities in the UK / USA?
- Which is the oldest university in the world?

b **11.1** Listen to the descriptions of Oxford University and Harvard University. Match the sentences with the universities. Write O or H.

1 ___ It is the oldest university in the English speaking world.
2 ___ It was founded in 1636.
3 ___ The University established its first Halls of Residence in the 13th Century.
4 ___ More than 18,000 students study here.
5 ___ It has one of the biggest libraries in the world.
6 ___ Women became members of the University in 1920.

c **11.1** Listen again and answer these questions.

1 Where is the city of Oxford?
2 Why did Oxford University develop rapidly from 1167 onwards?
3 Why did Oxford University establish Halls of Residence?
4 Who is Harvard University named after?
5 Why is the University named after him?
6 How big is the Harvard Library today?

2 READING & SPEAKING

a Read the article about applying to university in the UK and complete it with the words from below.

application   unconditional   offer
statement   courses   subject

Applying to University

If you want to go to university in the UK, you have to apply through the UCAS (University and Colleges Admissions Services) website. In most cases, your ¹_____ must be sent in by the middle of the January of the year you want to start university. You can choose up to five courses in different universities. UCAS sends your application to the universities of your choice, who decide whether or not to make you an ²_____ of a place. You receive offers or rejections from all five universities by 28th March. Some offers are conditional and depend on your grades in your school exams and some offers are ³_____.

When you apply, you also have to write a personal ⁴_____. This is a description of yourself and why you are interested in studying the subject you want to study.

In the UK, most degree ⁵_____ last between three and four years. You have to take exams each year, usually in June. At the end of the course, you take your final exams. If you pass, you get a Bachelor of Arts degree (BA), a Bachelor of Science degree (BSc), or a Bachelor of Education degree (BEd), depending on the ⁶_____ you studied.

b Read the article again and answer the questions.

1 What is UCAS?
2 When do you send your application to UCAS?
3 When do you know if you have a place at university?
4 What is the personal statement?
5 What are the names of degrees in the United Kingdom?

3 READING

a Read the introduction to the article. What is a 'gap' year?

b Now read all the article. Match the highlighted words with the definitions.

1 you don't know what's going to happen or what it will be like
2 start to feel comfortable doing something new
3 something you choose to do
4 connected with the sea and the creatures and plants that live there
5 the possibility of something happening

c In pairs, read the article again and answer the questions.

1 Where is Helen teaching?
2 Why was it hard for her at first?
3 What does she think of India?
4 What does Tom want to study at university?
5 Why did Tom decide to go to Mexico?
6 What skills has he learnt on his gap year?

What do you think?

✺ Do you want to go to university? Why (not)?
If so, what do you want to study? Why?
✺ Would you like to go to university abroad? Why (not)?
If so, where would you like to go?

PROJECT

Imagine you are planning a gap year when you finish school before starting to work or going to university.

Write a short essay (150 words) describing what you would like to do. Include information on:
• where you want to go
• what you want to do
• why you want to do this

In the UK, lots of students take a gap year before going to college or university. A gap year is a year out of study where they do something else. Many students take this opportunity to travel and work abroad. Many of them do voluntary work. It's a chance to get more experience, learn new skills and see a bit of the world. Helen and Tom are taking a gap year before going to University. Let's see what they have to say.

HELEN: *I'm spending my gap year teaching English in a school in the south of India. It's very interesting and I've made a lot of friends here. It was very hard at first, as we didn't have much training before we came but the students at*

the school were very friendly and we settled in quite quickly. India is a beautiful country, but it can be very chaotic and unpredictable so you have to be prepared. I like teaching children a lot and I think I'd like to become a teacher when I leave university.

TOM: *I want to study Marine Biology at university so I decided to come to Mexico on a marine conservation and research expedition. I'm nearly at the end of my nine months here and it has been the best experience on my life. I've learnt how to scuba dive and identify over a hundred types of fish. I also helped the local villagers rebuild their homes after a hurricane hit. I've learnt how valuable and fragile our environment is and how we must protect it. My Spanish is quite good now, too.*

1 LISTENING & SPEAKING

a In pairs, match the following sports with the photos:

___ canoeing ___ surfing ___ rugby ___ abseiling
___ parachuting ___ basketball

b In pairs, answer the questions.

- Have you ever tried any of these sports? Would you like to?

- What do you usually do during your summer holiday?

c **12.1** Look at the adverts for summer camps. Listen to Megan and George talking about their summer holiday. Which camps did they go to?

d Look at the adverts for summer camps again. Discuss in pairs which one would you like to go on and why?

ACTION AND ADVENTURE!

If you're looking for excitement this is the summer camp for you. We guarantee you'll have an action-packed week, with activities ranging from mountain biking to abseiling, parachuting to quad biking. There's also speed sailing for the more adventurous among you. There's no time to be bored at our summer camp!

A SPORTING CHANCE!

The opportunity to spend your whole summer playing the sports you love. We give you the chance to play over 20 different types of sports including football, basketball, volleyball, tennis and rugby. We also have professional coaches to help you practice your skills. You'll have a great time!

Make a splash!

Spend your summer at one of our wonderful water world camps. We'll make sure you have a fantastic time! We offer canoeing, raft building, surfing, windsurfing, wakeboarding and lots more. There are also 3 swimming pools on site and a variety of water slides. What better way to enjoy yourself this summer!

Art Attack!

We offer hundreds of fantastic creative opportunities on our summer camps. You can paint your own mug, design your own T-shirt, and make your own jewellery. These are just a few of the great activities on offer. So if you're tired of the usual summer sports camps, why not give Art Attack a try!

CULTURE

2 READING

a Look at the title of the article. What do you think it is about? Read the introduction. Why do some people think teenagers have too much free time?

b In pairs, try to guess the meaning of the highlighted words. Match them with their definitions.

1 busy
2 something that must be done because of a law or rule
3 without anyone in charge to make sure everything is safe / under control
4 difficult to control or manage
5 detailed arrangements and organised things someone is doing

c Now read the article and answer the questions.

1 How long is a typical school day in the UK?
2 Do British teenagers spend more time with their friends or their family?
3 Why do some people think after-school clubs will keep teenagers out of trouble?
4 What is the reason many schools don't do activities like drama and arts.
5 What do most students have to do after school?

What do you think?

* How long is the school day in your country?
* Do you go to any after-school clubs or activities? Why (not)?
* Do you think after-school clubs should be compulsory? Why (not)?

PROJECT

Write an email (100 words) to your friend describing what you would like to do for your next summer holiday. Include information on:
• where you want to go
• who you want to go with
• what you want to do

Too much free time?

In the UK, the school summer holidays are usually very long and many parents send their children to summer camps to keep them occupied. However, the summer holiday is not the only time young people need to be kept busy. School usually starts at 9 a.m. and finishes around 3.30 p.m. in the UK. Many people are concerned that this means students have too much unsupervised free time after school.

According to a recent study in the UK, British teenagers are the most badly behaved in Europe. They are more likely to drink, take drugs, join gangs and get into fights. They spend more time with their friends than with their parents or other adults. For example, only 64% of British teenagers eat an evening meal with their family, compared with 89% in France and 93% in Italy.

For some people the solution to this problem is to make after-school activities and clubs compulsory for all students, in order to keep them off the streets and out of trouble! They think this is a good way to make sure teenagers behave themselves. Schools often don't have time to do much drama, arts or sports during the day, so after-school clubs would give students the opportunity to enjoy these activities, too.

However, other people disagree. They say that the school day is already too long and it's not fair to expect students to stay after school hours. Most students also have homework to do. Also young people need some time to relax, not every minute of their free time needs to be planned, especially by their parents. They should be able to do what they like in their free time, within reason.

One thing is certain, a solution to the problem of Britain's unruly teenagers has to be found.

27

1 READING & SPEAKING

a In pairs, ask and answer the questions.

- How often do you listen to music?
- Do you watch MTV?
- What is your favourite music video?

b Read about MTV and complete the text with the correct verb in the right form.

promote   broadcast   continue   present   show
launch   see   accompany   play   base

c Cover the text. Mark the sentences T (true) or F (false). Correct the false sentences.

1 MTV is based in Los Angeles.

2 MTV launched in 1981.

3 The video presenters are called DJs.

4 The first video to be shown on MTV was *Thriller* by Michael Jackson.

5 *The Osbournes* is a reality show.

LADIES AND GENTLEMEN, ROCK AND ROLL!

MTV stands for Music Television. It is an American cable television network based in New York City. It was [1]_____ on the 1 August 1981. The idea behind the MTV channel was to show music videos and to become a point of reference of music events, news and promotions for artists and fans.

On 1 August 1981, at 12:01 a.m., MTV: Music Television launched with the words "Ladies and gentlemen, rock and roll!" Those words were [2]_____ by the original MTV theme song, playing over a film clip of the Apollo 11 moon landing. The first video [3]_____ on MTV was ***Video Killed the Radio Star*** by The Buggles. The VJs or Video jockeys presented the music videos.

In the 1980s, music videos were often promotional or concert clips. Then record companies [4]_____ the potential of MTV as a tool to gain recognition and publicity for musicians. So they began to create increasingly elaborate video clips specifically for the MTV network. Many bands and performers of the 1980s became famous on MTV including The Police, Duran Duran, Madonna and Michael Jackson. He became the first black artist to have a video on the channel. His 14-minute long music video for ***Thriller*** was often [5]_____ twice in an hour. In 1984 there were the first MTV Video Music Awards show.

During the 1990s MTV [6]_____ other programmes on its channel including a music news show and cartoons with mature themes, for example ***Beavis and Butt-head***. In 2002, MTV [7]_____ the first episode of a reality show called ***The Osbournes***. It is [8]_____ on the everyday life of Ozzy Osbourne and his children. Today, MTV [9]_____ a variety of music, pop culture, youth culture, and reality television shows and [10]_____ to be a point of reference for teenagers and young adults all over the world.

DVD 1 A radio actor

2 LISTENING & SPEAKING

a Prepare your answers to these questions.

1 What is the best concert you have ever seen?
2 What concert was it?
3 Where was it?
4 Who was taking part?
5 Were you there or did you see it on television?
6 What did you like about it?

b Ask and answer with a partner.

c **13.1** Read and listen to the text about Madonna. Then cover it and answer the questions below from memory.

1 What was Madonna's real name?
2 Where was she born?
3 Why did she leave home in 1978?
4 What other art forms is Madonna famous for?
5 What is the name of Madonna's fashion line?

d Cover the text. In pairs, can you remember what these numbers or dates refer to?

25	1963	1978	1980	35	1.2

What do you think?

* Do you download music from the Internet? Why (not)?
* Many people think the Internet is killing the music industry. Do you agree? Why (not)?

PROJECT

Write a short biography (100 words) about the life and career of your favourite pop star or group. Include information on:

• where they were born
• their life before they were famous
• why they are famous
• where they live now
• special achievements
• what you like about them

The Queen of Pop

One of the most famous and successful female singers in the history of pop music is Madonna. She became famous on MTV in the 1980s and continues to use MTV to market her music. Millions of young people go to her live performances all over the world which are both theatrical and musical productions. Her *Confessions* Tour in 2006 was one of the most successful tours ever by a female artist with a global audience of 1.2 million. For the past 25 years she has sold millions of copies of her albums world wide and her singles continue to reach number one in the music charts. Madonna is a very versatile artist and has also starred in films, written children's story books and has created a fashion line for the store H&M called *M by Madonna*.

Madonna Louise Ciccone was born in Bay City Michigan in 1958. Her father was an Italian-American from Pacentro in Abruzzo. She was raised in a catholic family. Madonna's mother died in 1963. As a child she persuaded her father to send her to ballet lessons and in 1978 when she finished high school she moved to New York to begin a dance career. Madonna said when she went to New York it was the first time she had ever flown. She went to New York with 35 dollars in her pocket. Today Madonna is one of the richest people in the world.

---

1 READING & SPEAKING

a In pairs, ask and answer the questions.

- Do you like shopping?
- Where do you go shopping?

Local shops   Town centre   Shopping centre
Supermarket   Internet   Market

- How much do you spend on shopping a month?

b Work in pairs, **A** and **B**. **A** read about Oxford Street, **B** read about Fifth Avenue.

c Share your information and complete the chart.

	Oxford Street	Fifth Avenue
Location		
Where the streets begin and end		
Famous Shops / Buildings		
Other information		

d What have the two streets got in common? What's different about them?

e Underline five words / phrases in either text that you want to remember.

2 WRITING

a Write an email to a penfriend about the main shopping street in your town or nearest town.

Include information on:

- Where it is
- How many shops it has
- Other information

Oxford Street

Oxford Street

Oxford Street in London's West End is 2km long and has over 300 shops. It is the world's longest shopping street! It begins at Marble Arch, goes through Oxford Circus and finishes at the junction between Charing Cross Road and Tottenham Court Road. It is the major shopping street in central London, but it is not the most expensive. Many department stores and hundreds of smaller shops are located on Oxford Street. *Selfridges* is one of the oldest and most famous department stores there. Other major stores are *Marks and Spencer*, *H&M*, *Niketown*, *Zara*, *Topshop*, and *GAP*. The *HMV* store at 150 Oxford Street, is Europe's largest music shop. At Christmas the street is decorated with Christmas lights. In November a famous actor or pop star turns on the lights and they remain on until 6 January. Oxford Street has four tube stations – Marble Arch, Bond Street, Oxford Circus and Tottenham Court Road.

Fifth Avenue

Fifth Avenue

3 LISTENING & SPEAKING

a Ask and answer with a partner.

- Does your town / region have a shopping centre?
- Where is it?
- How can you get there?
  How many shops has it got?
  What is your favourite shop there?

b **14.1** Listen to information about two shopping centres in the United Kingdom. Which shopping centre is the biggest?

c **14.1** Listen again and mark the sentences T (true) or F (false). Correct the false sentences.

1 The Metro Centre has 330 shops.
2 The Metro Centre is in Scotland.
3 You can watch films at the Metro Centre.
4 The Metro Centre is closed on Sunday.
5 Bluewater is near London.
6 You can go ice-skating at Bluewater.

Fifth Avenue is in the centre of Manhattan in New York City and is one of the main shopping streets in the world. Fifth Avenue begins at Washington Square Park in Greenwich Village and runs along the eastern side of Central Park and ends at the Harlem River at 142nd Street. It is the dividing line for streets in Manhattan which means it is the zero-numbering point for Manhattan's street addresses. Many famous shops are located on Fifth Avenue including *Tiffany* and *Cartier* the jewellers, *Abercrombie & Fitch* and Apple's glass cube, which is the entrance for its underground store. Many of New York's landmarks are on Fifth Avenue, including the Guggenheim Museum, the Metropolitan Museum of Art, the Empire State Building, the Rockefeller Centre, and Saint Patrick's Cathedral.

What do you think?

- Many shopping centres in the UK have a code of conduct. Some rules are that you must not swear; you must not wear clothing that covers your face (including hoods and baseball caps); you cannot walk around the centre in groups of more than five people without the intention to shop.
  Do you think this is a good idea? Why (not)?
- Do you like shopping centres? Why (not)?
- What are the advantages and disadvantages of shopping at a shopping centre?

PROJECT

Find out more information about the shopping area in your town or a town near you. Use the Internet or local newspapers to help you. Write an article (100 words) for a tourist guide book about it. Include information on:
- where the shopping area is
- what type of shops you can find there
- what else you can do there

Mind the Gap!

UNDERGROUND

The London Underground is the world's oldest and largest underground system and covers most of Greater London. It is called the Underground but about 55% of the network is above ground.

It has 275 stations and 12 interconnecting lines. Each line has a name and a colour to represent it on the underground map, for example the Victoria line is blue. The London Underground is also the longest underground system in the world, with over 408 km of track. Three million passengers travel on the London Underground every day. Londoners call the Underground the Tube, after its tube-shaped tunnels. The tube's first passenger trains started in 1863 on the Central line.

During the Blitz, the aerial bombing of London in World War II, Londoners hid from the bombs by using the underground stations as shelters during air raids and slept on platforms overnight. Air-raid sirens were a signal of approaching planes and for Londoners to hide in the underground stations.

The Underground does not run 24 hours a day. Track maintenance is done at night, after the system closes. The first trains start operating shortly after 5 a.m., running until around 1 a.m. Rush hour is from 7.30 a.m. to 9.30 a.m. and from 4.30 p.m. to 6.30 p.m.

London is divided into six travel zones. Zone one is the most central zone and zone six is the outer zone which includes Heathrow Airport. The more zones you cross the more you pay on the Underground. To travel on the Underground, you can buy a daily ticket, or a daily travel card or an Oyster card. This is a smart card with an electronic chip that you can charge with credit, and use to pay for travel on the Underground and on buses. It is the cheapest way of travelling in central London.

Most underground stations have escalators and stairs. The longest escalator in Europe is at Angel station on the Northern line, it is 60 m in length, with a vertical rise of 27.5 metres. People using the escalators stand on the right-hand side, so those in a hurry can walk past them on the left.

There are several safety announcements given to passengers who travel on the underground. When the doors of the trains are about to close you hear 'stand clear of the doors please'. When the train stops in a station where there is a gap between the train and the platform you can hear the famous phrase, 'Mind the Gap!'

1 READING & VOCABULARY

a In pairs, ask and answer these questions.

Which cities in your country have an underground rail system? Have you ever travelled on it?

b **15.1** Listen to and read the text.

What do you think 'Mind the Gap' means?

c Read the text again. In pairs, cover the text and ask and answer these questions.

1 Why do people call the underground the Tube?

2 How many passengers use the London Underground every day?

3 What was the Blitz? What was the underground used for during this period?

4 When is rush hour in London?

5 Is the London Underground open 24 hours a day?

6 What is an Oyster card?

d Read the text again and underline words that are connected with transport.

e Compare your list with your partner.

2 READING & SPEAKING

a In pairs, ask and answer the question.

What are the different forms of transport you can take in your town, or the nearest town to you?

b Read the text about transport in London. In pairs, match the phrases A–F with the correct paragraphs 1–6.

A Road traffic

B Air traffic

C River buses

D The Docklands Light Railway

E Commuter and Intercity railways

F The London Bus network

c In pairs, find definitions for the following words in the text:

1 A person who travels a long distance to work every day. _____

2 To get on a bus. _____

3 A flight with a regular service and timetable.
   _____   _____

4 A short distance flight. _____

5 Blocked roads. _____

What do you think?

✹ Look at the different ways of getting around in London. Which is the most environmentally friendly? Why?

✹ Which of these forms of transport have you travelled on?

✹ What is your favourite form of transport? Why?

PROJECT

Write a short article (100 words) for a tourist guide book describing transport in your town or the nearest large town to you. Include information on:

• different types of transport
• stations
• the cheapest / most expensive form of transport
• what the advantages and disadvantages of each type of transport are

GETTING AROUND LONDON

1 _____ is a twenty-four hour service and has over 700 routes. Six million people use the buses in London each week. Red Double Decker buses are internationally recognized! On most buses you can buy your ticket from the driver, but it is cheaper to buy an Oyster card. If you are under 16 or over 60 years of age you do not pay on the buses or underground in London.

2 _____ is a second metro system using small and light trains without a driver. This serves East London and Greenwich and is important for commuters to the financial district of London, Canary Wharf.

3 _____ do not cross the city but run into 14 terminal railway stations around the historic centre of London. These stations link London with other cities in the United Kingdom. Eurostar trains link London with Paris and Brussels.

4 _____ in London passes through one of five airports. London Heathrow is the busiest airport in the world for international traffic and scheduled passenger flights on long and short-haul journeys. London Gatwick, London Stansted, and London Luton cater mostly for low-cost and short-haul flights and London City airport is mainly for business travellers and private jet traffic.

5 _____ in London is limited in the centre by the congestion charge, introduced to reduce traffic volumes in the city centre. Motorists pay a daily charge to drive their cars in the centre. London has an outer orbital motorway called the M25.

6 _____ take commuters along the River Thames from Westminster to Greenwich. Many workers in the city of London use this form of transport to get to and from work.

1 READING & SPEAKING

a In pairs, look at the eight photos.

Do you recognize these famous monuments? Write the name and the country under each one. What do they all have in common?

b 16.1 Listen and read the text below and check your answers to **a**.

c Which words in the text mean the following?

1 traditions and qualities that a country has had for many years
2 treated like a member without actually belonging to group
3 causing a lot of public discussion and disagreement
4 asking money for something
5 to show unhappiness about something
6 feelings or thoughts about something

d Read the text again. In pairs, answer the questions.

1 What was the point of the competition?
2 How could people vote?
3 Why didn't everyone agree with the results?
4 How many votes came from Jordan?
5 What helped people vote more in Brazil?
6 How was it a global competition?

The New SEVEN WONDERS OF THE WORLD

Over 2000 years ago the Greeks made a list of Seven Wonders of the Ancient World, all situated around the Mediterranean Sea. Out of the seven, only one remains today: the Great Pyramid of Giza. In 2006, a private organization in Switzerland decided to have a competition to decide the New Seven Wonders of the World. The aims of the competition were to draw attention to the world's cultural heritage and to highlight the importance of preserving these special places.

People could vote for their favourite site by phone, text or Internet. According to the organizers, there were more than 100 million votes from all over the world. They announced the following winners in July 2007: the Colosseum in Italy, Chichen Itza in Mexico, the Taj Mahal in India, Petra in Jordan, Machu Picchu in Peru, The Statue of Christ the Redeemer in Brazil, and The Great Wall of China. The Pyramids of Giza were an honorary 'New' Seven Wonder.

e In pairs, match the information (A–H) with the monument (1–8).

A It's the largest man-made monument in the world.

B It's situated on a mountain in the Andes.

C It took 5 years to build.

D It's on the edge of the Arabian Desert.

E It was the centre of the Mayan civilisation.

F Cruel fights and games took place in this arena.

G It was built in memory of a Persian princess.

H It's 146m high and probably took over 20 years to build.

1 Colosseum

2 Chichen Itza

3 Great Pyramid of Giza

4 Great Wall of China

5 Taj Mahal

6 Machu Picchu

7 Statue of Christ the Redeemer

8 Petra

2 LISTENING

a **16.2** Listen to a short description of four of the runners-up.
Number them in the order you hear them. Write in the country, and any interesting facts.

Location	Country	Interesting facts
a ____ The Eiffel Tower		
b ____ Stonehenge		
c ____ The Sydney Opera House		
d ____ The Statue of Liberty		

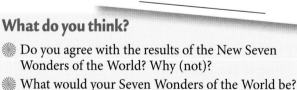

However, the results were controversial for a number of reasons. People could vote as many times as they liked which meant the results weren't very accurate. For example, the population of Jordan is under 7 million people, but there were over 14 million votes from the country! In Brazil, telephone companies stopped charging people for the phone calls and text messages in order to encourage them to vote. Some people complained that not everyone in the world has access to modern technology and the results only reflected the opinions of those who use the Internet.

Whether you agree with the final winners or not, one thing is certain, it was the first global competition of its kind!

What do you think?

* Do you agree with the results of the New Seven Wonders of the World? Why (not)?
* What would your Seven Wonders of the World be?

PROJECT

Choose one of your New Seven Wonders of the World. Write a short description (100 words) of it for a school magazine. Include information about:

• where it is

• who built it

• what was is used for

• why you think it should be included on the list

1 READING & SPEAKING

a In pairs, ask and answer the questions.

- Have you been to any art galleries?
- Which did you visit?
- Did you enjoy your visit? Why (not)?

b In pairs, match the artists with the country and genre

A	Andy Warhol	1	Germany	i	Surrealism
B	Wassily Kandinsky	2	Spain	ii	Cubism
C	Pablo Picasso	3	Russia	iii	Abstraction
D	Max Ernst	4	America	iv	Pop Art

c Read the article about the Tate Modern and check your answers to **b**.

d Look at the highlighted words in the text and choose the correct meaning.

1 belonging to the present time
2 arranged in the order in which they happened
3 a piece of modern sculpture that can be made using sound, light or objects
4 the side of a river
5 Groups of people who share the same ideas or aims
6 a machine to generate electricity

e Cover the text. In pairs, can you remember what these numbers or dates refer to? Make a sentence about each number.

2000	1981	200	99	5

f Read the text again. In pairs, answer the questions.

1 Where is Tate Modern?
2 Who designed the original building?
3 What is the Turbine Hall used for?
4 How are they planning to extend Tate Modern?
5 How does Tate Modern organise its galleries?
6 Where are the other Tate galleries?

Tate Modern is Britain's national museum of international modern art. It is in London, on the south bank of the River Thames, opposite St Paul's Cathedral and the City of London. It displays examples of modern art from 1900 to the present day.

Tate Modern opened in 2000. The building was originally the Bankside Power Station, designed by Sir Giles Gilbert Scott, who also designed Waterloo Bridge and the famous British red telephone box. The power station closed in 1981 and architects Herzog and de Meuron helped convert it into an art gallery. The building is more than 200 metres long and its chimney is 99 metres high. There are 5 levels and the vast Turbine Hall. This is where the Tate displays large installations by contemporary artists. One famous example of an installation was a series of huge slides that visitors could go down, leading from the different levels of the building to the hall floor. This, and other popular installations, has helped capture the imagination of the public, and Tate Modern is now one of the biggest tourist attractions in London. There are plans to build a glass pyramid extension, dedicated to photography and video exhibitions.

Many art galleries arrange art chronologically, but Tate Modern organises its works of art according to the important movements in twentieth century art. There is Abstraction, with paintings by artists like Wassily Kandinsky; Surrealism, including artists like Salvador Dali and Max Ernst; Cubism, including works by Picasso; and Pop Art, represented by artists like Andy Warhol.

There are 3 other Tate galleries – Tate Britain (also in London), Tate Liverpool and Tate St Ives, in Cornwall. Tate Modern is, however, the most popular.

TATE MODERN

2 READING

a Complete the descriptions (A–D) with the words from the box.

> culture   geometric   images   United States
> dream   realistic   science   ideas

A A style of art, developed in the 1950s and 60s, that started in Britain and the ¹_____. Artists use materials from the everyday world of popular ²_____, such as comic strips, canned goods, Hollywood movies, and ³_____ fiction.

B A style and movement in art and literature in which ⁴_____ and events that are not connected are put together in a strange or impossible way, like in a ⁵_____, to try to express what is happening deep in the mind.

C A style and movement of art in which objects and people are represented as ⁶_____ shapes, often shown from many different angles at the same time.

D A style and movement in art not representing people or things in a ⁷_____ way, but expressing the artist's ⁸_____ about them.

b Match the descriptions (A–D) with the headings (1–4).

1 ___Surrealism
2 ___Cubism
3 ___Abstraction
4 ___Pop Art

3 LISTENING & SPEAKING

a **17.1** Listen and complete the fact file about British artist, Antony Gormley.

Name _____
Born _____
Nationality _____
Subject studied _____
Prizes won _____

b **17.1** Listen again and mark the sentences T (true), F (false) or DS (doesn't say). Correct the false ones.

1 Antony came from a small family.
2 In the 1970s, he started painting pictures of India.
3 He is interested the connections between people.
4 Most of his work is in art galleries.
5 *Event Horizon* is displayed in Liverpool.
6 *Waste Man* was burnt by Antony Gormley.

What do you think?
* Are you interested in art? Why (not)?
* Who is your favourite artist? Why?

PROJECT

Write a description (100 words) of a famous artist. Include information on:
• their life
• their education
• famous works
• where you can see their work today

1 READING & SPEAKING

a In pairs, ask and answer the questions.

Where did you go on holiday last summer?

How did you get there?

How long did it take to get there?

b Read the introduction to the article. What is it about?

Is it a good idea to fly?

The huge increase in air traffic in recent years means more people are flying than ever before. But concern over air travel and global warming has put the airline industry in the spotlight. We asked two experts their opinions on the connection between the two.

1 KATE HARDIE, CLIMATE CHANGE CAMPAIGNER

Aviation is the world's fastest growing man-made source of carbon dioxide and it is a major contributor to global warming. It is more dangerous than other types of pollutants such as cars, because the carbon dioxide enter the ozone layer immediately, causing more damage. We should be flying less, but millions of people are taking advantage of the budget airlines' cheap flights to travel more. It makes no environmental sense that it is often cheaper and quicker to fly from London to Scotland than it is to go by train. We need to reduce the number of cheap flights and encourage people to travel by train and to go on holiday nearer to home. The Government could help by increasing the tax on aviation fuel. The people who live in places like Europe and the USA fly the most; they should pay more for the pollution they are causing to the planet.

2 DR IAN TAYLOR, AVIATION STUDIES COMMISSION

People complain a lot about air travel these days, but it actually accounts for less than 5% of carbon dioxide emissions. Introducing higher taxes won't solve the problem. If prices go up, only rich people will be able to travel which isn't fair. More air travel means more tourism, which creates millions of jobs all over the world. These jobs are especially important in developing countries, many of which lack alternative sources of income. If people stop flying there could be massive global unemployment which would affect the poorer countries most. We are making planes more energy-efficient and encouraging fuller flights with shorter flight routes. It's also possible to make your flight 'carbon neutral' by offsetting the amount of carbon emissions it produces. This means you pay money to support initiatives such as planting trees or which consume CO_2 or energy-saving projects that reduce carbon emissions elsewhere which cancel out the amount of carbon your flight produces. It's only natural that people want to travel and explore the world and they should be able to.

c Now read all the article. Match the highlighted words or phrases with the definitions.

1 the money that a person or country earns from work or from investments
2 using one cost to cancel or reduce the effect of another
3 material that produces heat or power when burnt
4 not producing any carbon
5 a substance that pollutes
6 low in price

d Student **A** read text 1, Student **B** read text 2. Write notes in the chart summarizing the main points.

A Arguments against air travel	B Arguments for air travel

e Share your information. Now complete the chart.

f Now read the text again. Mark the sentences T (true), F (false) or DS (doesn't say). Correct the false sentences.

1 People are flying less because flights cost more.
2 Planes pollute the atmosphere more than cars.
3 More people are going on holiday close to home.
4 It's sometimes cheaper to travel by plane than by train.
5 Air travel helps promote tourism.
6 Planting trees can offset the amount of carbon your flight produces.

2 LISTENING

a 18.1 Listen to another expert talking about offsetting carbon emissions by planting trees.

Does she think it's a good idea?

b 18.1 Listen again and answer these questions.

1 Why do some travel companies say you can fly without worrying about pollution?
2 What happens when a tree dies?
3 How are local people sometimes affected by tree planting initiatives?
4 Why do lots of the trees that the companies plant die?
5 Why is tree planting sometimes bad for the local environment?
6 What is the best solution, according to the expert?

What do you think?
* Is carbon-offsetting a good idea? Why (not)?
* What other ways are there to save energy?

PROJECT

How carbon-neutral are you? For example, do you travel to school by car, by bus, by train or on foot? Write a short report (150 words) explaining the ways in which you use energy in the home and at school. Include information on:
• how you travel to school
• where you go on holiday
• ways in which you can try to save energy

1 READING & SPEAKING

a In pairs, ask and answer the questions.

- Have you ever been in love?
- Do you want to get married one day?
- Do you think people should marry for love or marry for money?

b Read the text, and match the highlighted words with their meanings.

1 all the money and property that someone leaves behind when they die

2 an amount of money or property which in some countries, a woman's family gives to the man she is marrying

3 a change which makes the quality of life better

4 the state of being husband and wife

5 an attitude or an opinion about something

6 a man who has not married

7 to receive property or money from someone who dies

c In pairs. Read the text again and mark the sentences T (true) or F (false). Correct the false sentences.

1 *Pride and Prejudice* is a historical novel.

2 The Bennets had six daughters.

3 Mr Darcy is very poor.

4 When Mr Bennet dies his estate will pass to his cousin.

5 Elizabeth does not have a good first impression of Darcy.

6 Elizabeth marries Darcy at the end of the story.

2 LISTENING & READING

a **19.1** Listen to and read the first chapter of *Pride and Prejudice*. What are Mr and Mrs Bennet talking about?

b Read the extract again and answer the questions.

1 Who is the Bennets' new neighbour?

2 How does the author describe Mr Bingley?

3 How does Mrs Bennet describe Mr Bingley?

4 What plans does Mrs Bennet have for Mr Bingley?

5 Why must Mr Bingley see the girls as soon as possible?

PRIDE AND PREJUDICE

Pride and Prejudice by Jane Austen was published in 1813. Like all of her novels *Pride and Prejudice* is a comedy of manners which describes in detail the customs, behaviours and habits of people. In 18th century English there was a class system which parallels the social class system of today. Women usually married men of the same class. For the upper-classes, marriage was much more like a business transaction than it is today. Even among poor families marriage contracts could include financial conditions and a dowry. Marriage was the only way of social improvement for a woman.

The novel tells the story of the Bennet family in Hertfordshire who try to overcome social barriers that separate them from their aristocratic neighbours. Mrs Bennet wants to find husbands for her five daughters, Jane, Elizabeth, Lydia, Kitty, and Mary because when her husband dies his estate will go to his cousin Mr Collins and so her daughters will inherit nothing. She is very happy when Charles Bingley, a rich young bachelor goes to live near them with his two sisters and rich friend Mr Darcy. Bingley falls in love with Jane and Darcy is attracted to her sister Elizabeth. At first, Elizabeth does not like Darcy as she thinks he is arrogant. But, when Lydia runs away with Mr Wickham, Mr Darcy convinces them to return and marry to protect the family honour. As time passes Elizabeth falls in love with Darcy and the novel ends with Elizabeth accepting his proposal of marriage and Jane marrying Bingley.

3 LISTENING & SPEAKING

a In pairs, answer the questions.

- What is the difference between an arranged marriage and a love marriage?
- Which type of marriage do you think is best? Why?

b **19.2** Listen to the report on arranged marriages in the United Kingdom.

1 What is the difference between an arranged marriage and a forced marriage?

c **19.2** Listen again and complete the sentences.

1 People choose their own marriage partner
_____.

2 Many Indian families who have settled outside India still _____.

3 Supporters of the custom say that divorce
_____.

4 Being part of two cultures _____.

5 Many young Indian people living in Britain know that one day they will _____.

6 Many families discuss the issue
_____.

7 Some families ask matchmakers to help them
_____.

8 Parents consider educational background and
_____ to choose the bride and grooms.

What do you think?

※ Do you think arranged marriages are a good idea? Why (not)?

※ 'Marriage is not important in the modern world.' Do you agree? Why (not)?

PROJECT

Pride and Prejudice is a novel about love. Choose a film, book or play about love and write a review (150 words) for a school magazine. Include information on:
- the characters
- the setting
- the plot
- the ending

Pride and Prejudice

CHAPTER 1

The Bennets' new neighbour

0 It is a truth well known to all the world that an unmarried man in possession of a large fortune must be in need of a wife. And when such a man moves into a neighbourhood, even if nothing is known about his feelings or opinions,
5 this truth is so clear to the surrounding families, that they think of him immediately as the future husband of one or other of their daughters.

'My dear Mr Bennet,' said Mrs Bennet to her husband one day, 'have you heard that someone is going to rent
10 Netherfield Park at last?'

'No, Mrs Bennet, I haven't,' said her husband.

'Don't you want to know who is renting it?' cried Mrs Bennet impatiently.

'You want to tell me, and I don't mind listening.'

15 Mrs Bennet needed no further encouragement. 'Well, my dear, I hear that he's a very rich young man from the north of England. It seems he came to see Netherfield on Monday and was so delighted with it that he arranged to rent it at once. Of course, it is the finest house in the
20 area, with the largest gardens. His servants will be here by the end of the week, and he will be arriving soon afterwards!'

'What is his name?' asked Mr Bennet.

'Bingley.'

25 'Is he married or single?'

'Oh, single, my dear of course! A single man of large fortune – he has an income of four or five thousand pounds a year. How wonderful for our girls!'

'Why? How can it affect them?' Mr Bennet asked.

30 'My dear Mr Bennet,' she replied, 'how can you be so annoying! You must realize I'm thinking of his marrying one of our daughters.'

'Is that his purpose in coming to the area?'

35 'His purpose? No, of course not. But it's very likely that he'll fall in love with one of them. And I want him to see the girls as soon as possible, before our
40 other neighbours introduce themselves.

Taken from *Oxford Bookworms Library level 6 Pride and Prejudice*

1 READING

a In pairs, answer the questions.

- Where do you think the clothes you are wearing come from?
- Look at the labels and check.
- Do you think they were hand-made or produced in a factory?

b Read the article and put the phrases A–F in the correct places.

A the textile industry

B because of a series of inventions

C effects spread throughout

D started in Britain

E are hand-made

F on society was enormous

Textiles and the Industrial Revolution

Today, very few of the products we use in our everyday lives [1]_____. Of course, it wasn't always like this. In the past, almost everything was hand-made and the factory system we have today did not exist. This change from the world of artisans to factories, and all its associated benefits, is called the Industrial Revolution.

It [2]_____ in the early 1700s. At that time, the production of woollen textiles was a very important British industry. For most of the 18th century, more than a quarter of British exports were woollen products. During the Industrial Revolution, [3]_____ went from a relatively small collection of weavers in their homes, working with handlooms and spinning wheels,

to a major mainstream industry which produced clothing on a large scale.

This happened [4]_____, starting with the flying shuttle in 1733. This was an improvement to looms that helped weavers to weave faster. In 1764, two other inventions helped speed up the process even more: The Spinning Jenny, a machine which improved the spinning wheel and the Water Frame, the first powered textile machine.

The impact of the Industrial Revolution [5]_____. In just over a century, Britain went from a rural, agricultural-based economy to one of industrialized towns and factories. The [6]_____ Western Europe and North America during the 19th century, eventually affecting most of the world.

c Read the article again. Match the highlighted words with the definitions.

1 a person whose job is to make textiles

2 a pointed tool used to pull a thread backwards and forwards over other threads

3 a large wheel, operated by foot, for twisting wool

4 a person who does skilled work, making things with their hands

5 the advantages or useful effects as a result of something

6 a machine for making textiles, operated by hand

2 LISTENING & SPEAKING

a **20.1** Listen to the descriptions of two inventions which revolutionised the textile industry and complete the chart.

Inventor	Invention	When

b **20.1** Listen again and mark the sentences T (true) or F (false). Correct the false ones.

1 Weavers used to pass the shuttle backwards and forwards across the loom by hand.

2 The flying shuttle needed two people to operate it.

3 John Kay's invention was very popular with textile workers.

4 The Spinning Jenny allowed weavers to spin eight threads instead of one at the same time.

5 Hargreaves made a lot of money from his invention.

6 People were using thousands of Spinning Jenny's in Britain in the late 1770s.

What do you think?

❋ Was the textile industry important in your country? Why (not)?

❋ Where were the main centres?

❋ Is it an important industry now? Why (not)?

PROJECT

Using the Internet, find out as much as you can about the Industrial Revolution in your country. Write a short essay (150 words). Include information on:

• when it started

• famous inventions

• the effects it had on the country

1 READING & SPEAKING

a In pairs, ask and answer the questions.

- When was your last holiday?
- Where did you go?
- What are the top five places to visit in your country?

b In pairs, predict the answers to these questions.

1 What is a tourist?
2 What percentage of the world's workers are employed in the tourist industry?
3 What is the most visited city in the world?
4 What is the most visited monument in the world?

c Read the text and check your answers.

d Read the article again and answer these questions.

1 How many international visits are made every year?
2 Which factors have helped the growth of tourism?
3 How is tourism important for some countries?
4 What are some of the negative effects of tourism?

2 READING & VOCABULARY

a Read about 21st century tourism and put the headings A–F in the right place.

A Hobby and learning-oriented tourism
B Sports holidays
C Underwater hotels
D Ecotourism / Agricultural tourism
E Sustainable tourism
F Space tourism

b In pairs, ask and answer the question.

Which of these holidays would you like to go on? Why (not)?

TOURISM

A tourist is someone who visits a place for pleasure. Globally, 635 million international visits are made every year by tourists. Tourism is one of the world's largest and fastest growing industries. It employs 10 percent of the world's workforce. This growth has resulted from improvements in transport, higher incomes and people having longer holidays and spending more on them. Why?

- Changing transport – improved roads and increased car ownership; introduction of large jet aircraft and more airports.
- Changing costs – Travel companies offer cheap organized package holidays, airlines offer very cheap flights.
- Changing work patterns – people have more leisure time, flexible hours and paid holidays.
- Changing attitudes – people are now 'expected' to have at least one holiday a year. Advertising encourages us to take holiday, and to spend money on them.

Tourism is vital for many countries because of the income generated by the consumption of goods and services by tourists, and the opportunity for employment in the service industries associated with tourism – for example hotels and transport.

Currently Paris is the most visited city in the world, with many of these visitors heading to the Eiffel Tower – the worlds most visited monument.

21st century tourism

1 _____ is becoming more popular as people realize the terrible effects poorly planned tourism can have on communities. Mass tourism can have negative impacts on the environment and on local people and their culture. On these holidays tour guides take tourists to different places so that the environment is protected.

2 _____ include adventure holidays for example mountaineering and hiking, scuba diving, skiing, or to see special event for example the Football World Cup or the Olympic games.

3 _____ includes walking tours, cookery courses, wine tasting holidays, history classes, dance holidays, photography holidays, garden tours.

4 _____ is expected to 'take off' in the first quarter of the 21st century, but the number of tourists in orbit will remain low until technologies such as a space elevator make space travel cheap.

5 _____ for example Hydropolis in Dubai, will mean that people can stay in a hotel in the seas of the Persian Gulf, with windows providing views of marine life.

6 _____ where the main attractions are ecological resources for example a working farm, or a nature reserve.

3 LISTENING & SPEAKING

a **21.1** A national park is a place which preserves the natural beauty, wildlife and cultural heritage of an area. There are 14 national parks in the UK.

1 Listen to Mary and John talk about the national park where they live.

2 Do they think tourism is positive or negative? Compare what you understood with your partner.

b **21.1** Listen again and fill in the table with the information about the Yorkshire Dales national park.

Location	
Size	
Number of visitors every year	
Number of local residents	
Attractions	

c Who do you agree with, Mary or John?

What do you think?

✹ What is your favourite tourist attraction in your country? Give reasons for your answer.

✹ Are there any national parks in your country? Where are they? What are the advantages and disadvantages of tourism for them?

PROJECT

Write an email (100 words) to a friend about your last holiday. Include information on:
• where you went
• how long you were there for
• a description of the place
• where you stayed
• what you did there

Loch Lomond and The Trossachs
Northumberland
North York Moors
Lake District
Yorkshire Dales
Peak District
The Broads
Snowdonia
Pembrokeshire Coast
Brecon Beacons
Exmoor
New Forest
South Downs
Dartmoor

1 READING, LISTENING & SPEAKING

a In pairs, ask and answer the questions.

- Who were Guglielmo Marconi and Thomas Edison?
- What do you know about them?
- What did they invent?

b Read the eight facts about the lives of two inventors. In pairs, decide which four are about Guglielmo Marconi and which four are about Thomas Edison. Write M or E.

c 22.1 Listen and Check.

d In pairs, write the facts about Edison and Marconi in the right order to form a paragraph about the lives of each inventor. Listen again and check your answers.

GUGLIELMO MARCONI AND THOMAS EDISON

1 ___ In 1882, he switched on the first steam generating power station at Holborn Viaduct in London. This provided electricity supplies to street lamps and several private houses within a short distance.

2 ___ He tried to interest the Italian Ministry of Posts and Telegraphs in his invention, but they were not interested so he went to England. In 1896, he met the Engineer-in-Chief of the British Post Office and he demonstrated his wireless signals in London and on Salisbury Plain.

3 ___ He was born near Bologna in 1874. As a boy he was very interested in physics. In 1895, he began laboratory experiments in his father's house and he succeeded in sending wireless signals over a distance of nearly two kilometres.

4 ___ He received the Nobel prize for physics in 1909. In 1931 he began research into shorter waves, resulting in the opening in 1932 of the world's first microwave radiotelephone link between the Vatican City and the Pope's summer residence at Castel Gandolfo.

5 ___ He was born in Milan, Ohio in 1847.

6 ___ In 1897, he obtained a patent and established the Wireless Telegraph and Signal Company Limited, which opened the world's first radio factory in England in 1898. In 1901, he demonstrated that wireless waves were not affected by the curvature of the Earth and he transmitted his first wireless signals across the Atlantic between Cornwall and Newfoundland.

7 ___ He developed many devices that greatly influenced life around the world including the phonograph and the long lasting light bulb. He was one of the first inventors to apply the principles of mass production to the process of invention.

8 ___ He made the first public demonstration of his incandescent light bulb on December 1879. He famously said "We will make electricity so cheap that only the rich will burn candles".

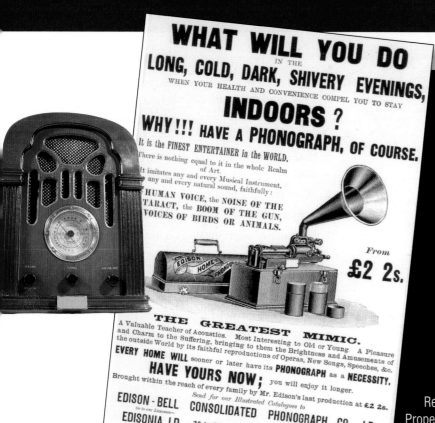

A NATION OF INNOVATION

Recent statistics released by the UK Intellectual Property Office, where details of all new inventions are registered, have shown that over the last few years numbers of inventions are on the increase. The office used to receive 500 applications per month from individual inventors, but has seen this figure rise to almost 900 a month.

Experts believe that this growth is partly due to new opportunities provided by the digital age. Nowadays it is easy to download information on how things work, or to design products for your own lifestyle. Because of this, people have become more interested in creating their own products. Another reason for the change could be the growing interest from TV companies. Programmes such as *Dragon's Den*, where inventors try to find financial support for their ideas and inventions, are increasingly popular worldwide. There are versions of the series in eight countries, including Australia, Canada, the UK, and Japan.

Many new inventions can go on to change the world we live in, making their inventors very rich in the process. But the majority disappear without a trace.

2 READING

a Read the text. Mark the sentences T (true), F (false) or DS (doesn't say). Correct the false sentences.

1 The number of inventions registered in the UK has gone up.
2 Most of the inventors are men.
3 The Internet has had a big effect on the number of people inventing things.
4 There is a global interest in TV programmes about inventions and ideas.
5 Most inventors make a lot of money from their ideas.

What do you think?

☀ Which invention was more important the radio or the light bulb? Give reasons for your answers.

PROJECT

Using the Internet or books to help you write a report (100 words) about an invention that you think has changed our lives. Include information on:
• what the invention is
• who invented it
• when it was invented
• how it has changed our lives

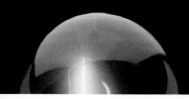

1 SPEAKING & LISTENING

a In pairs, ask and answer the questions.

- What's your favourite food?
- What's your least favourite food?
- How much fruit do you eat a day?
- Do you think the following factors influence what we eat? Give reasons for your answers.

age	yes/no	_____
where we live	yes/no	_____
job	yes/no	_____
religion	yes/no	_____

- What other factors can influence our diet?

b The food pyramid represents how much of each food type we need in a healthy balanced diet.

Match the correct food type (A–F) to the sections of the pyramid (1–6).

A ~~Fruit~~
B Oils, fats & sugars
C Protein
D Dairy
E Carbohydrates
F Vegetables

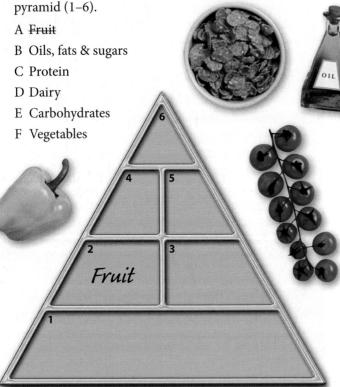

c Now put the following food into the correct section of the food pyramid.

chicken pasta rice pears tuna yogurt
mayonnaise chocolate courgettes
potatoes bacon milk

d **23.1** Listen to a dietician talking about a healthy diet and the food pyramid. Check your answers to c.

e **23.1** Listen again. In pairs, answer these questions.

1 How many portions of carbohydrates should we eat a day?
2 What size is a portion?
3 Why are carbohydrates important?
4 How many portions of fruit and vegetables should we eat?
5 What do fruit and vegetables provide the body with?
6 Why is calcium important?
7 How much protein should we eat?
8 How often should we eat foods with added fat or sugar?

f Re-order the words to make sentences. Then mark the sentences T (true) or F (false). Correct the false sentences.

1 grill should instead you or frying food bake of it.
2 add are when should you to food salt cooking you.
3 fruit eat you day portions of should and vegetables a three.
4 you eat healthy foods have a variety of in order should to a diet.
5 should teeth sugary your brush you eating snacks after.
6 every should you breakfast day eat.

2 READING & SPEAKING

a Look at the photo. What do you think the article is about?

b Read the article and tick [✓] the sentence which best describes what the article is about.

1 How bad school food is in the UK.
2 How important food and nutrition is in schools in the UK.

c Read the text and put the phrases A–E in the correct places.

A fizzy drinks, chocolate and crisps
B you are more likely to suffer from
C very negative effects on concentration and behaviour
D buy junk food outside school
E schools are still not providing

DVD 2 Healthy living

8 Earth Sciences Rubbish and recycling

1 LISTENING & SPEAKING

a In pairs, ask and answer the questions.

- What do you do with your rubbish?
- Which of the following do you recycle?

> paper glass plastic shoes
> clothes chewing gum

- Who recycles the most, you or your partner?

b **24.1** Listen to the man talking about household rubbish. What time of the year do we produce the most rubbish?

c In pairs, try to guess the meaning of these words. Match them with their definitions.

1	raw materials	a place where rubbish is buried
2	waste	put in bins
3	landfill site	rubbish, things to be thrown out
4	soil	a promise
5	thrown out	earth
6	resolution	something unchanged, in its natural state

d **24.1** Listen again and choose a, b, or c.

1 Households in the UK…

  a recycle a lot of rubbish.

  b produce a lot of rubbish.

  c produce and recycle a lot of rubbish.

2 Landfill sites are not a good way to dispose of rubbish because…

  a they are very large.

  b there are not enough of them.

  c they cause pollution.

3 We need to change our habits and…

  a reduce the amount of rubbish we produce, recycle more.

  b produce more rubbish and recycle more.

  c reduce the amount of rubbish we produce and use more raw materials.

e In pairs, listen again and check your answers.

f In pairs, match the Christmas facts (A–E) with the suggestions on how we can waste less (1–5).

A We send approximately 150 million Christmas cards each day at Christmas.

B We buy millions of Christmas trees every Christmas.

C People buy hundreds of kilometres of wrapping paper to wrap their presents.

D We use lots more bottles, glass containers and cans over the Christmas period.

E We often buy presents that are unwanted or which break easily.

1 Give money or gift vouchers to avoid unwanted presents. Buy gifts which are durable. Things which break easily will just end up in the bin and cannot be reused by anybody.

2 Buy recycled wrapping paper and use string or ribbon instead of sticky tape to wrap gifts. The string and paper can then be reused.

3 Buy drinks in large containers, rather than lot of small ones. One large bottle creates less waste than a lot of little ones and it's more economical.

4 Buy a tree with roots that can be planted in your garden or kept in a pot for next year. You can use an artificial tree, but it's difficult to recycle as it's made of lots of different materials.

5 Recycle your Christmas cards. Shops and supermarkets have special bins where you can put your cards. You could also send electronic Christmas cards instead!

A sticky problem

Many young people don't think twice before dropping their chewing gum on the floor and probably don't even think of it as rubbish. It's estimated that there are more than 300,000 pieces of chewing gum on London's famous Oxford Street alone. City councils in the UK spend millions of pounds each year cleaning the gum off pavements and streets.

Some councils are taking action. They have put 'gummy bins' along streets and outside places such as clubs or bars where people are likely to drop gum. Gummy bins are specially-designed rubbish bins for chewing gum only. They come in attractive bright colours that are easy to see and they are also much cheaper than cleaning the streets. The chewing gum is recycled and used for things such as drainage systems for football pitches.

Scientists are also working to try and solve the problem with several ideas including biodegradable chewing gum and non-stick chewing gum, which is easier to remove from pavements.

However, some people think the chewing gum manufacturers should take more responsibility for the problem too. Money from the sale of chewing gum could go towards cleaning up the streets. Gum manufacturers are obviously not very enthusiastic about this approach! They say the problem is with the people who drop the gum in the first place. They should be given large fines and encouraged to use bins instead. Whatever the best solution is, it certainly is a sticky problem!

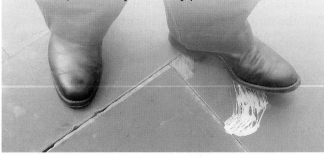

2 SPEAKING & READING

a Read the article about chewing gum. Why is it a problem?

b Read the text again. Then cover it and answer the questions below from memory.

1 How much money do councils spend each year cleaning chewing gum off the streets?
2 What is a 'gummy bin'?
3 What is recycled chewing gum used for?
4 Why is non-stick gum better?
5 How could gum manufacturers help?
6 Who do the gum manufacturers blame for the problem?

c Read the text again and underline five possible solutions to the problem of chewing gum.

What do you think

※ Do you chew gum? What do you do with it when you finish chewing?
※ Is chewing gum a problem in your school / your town?
※ Do you recycle much? Why (not)?

PROJECT

Find out more about recycling in your area. Write a short article (150 words) for a school magazine summarizing your findings. Include information on:
• what materials people can recycle
• how these materials are collected
• what these materials are used for

1 READING & VOCABULARY

a In pairs, ask and answer the questions.

- Where are your parents and grandparents from?
- Do you know any one who has moved to another town / country? Why did they move?

b Complete the text with headings A–E.

A Refugees

B Rural-Urban migration

C International migration

D Internal Migration

E Counter-Urbanization

c Match the highlighted words or phrases with their meanings.

1 the money that a person receives for the work they have done

2 a large amount of water that spreads from a river or the sea, covering an area which should be dry

3 the amount of money and level of comfort that a particular person or group has

4 a danger or a risk

5 something that makes a town or a place easy to live in

d In pairs, cover the text and answer the questions from memory.

1 What is the difference between immigration and emigration?

2 What is a push factor?

3 What is a pull factor?

4 Name the different types of immigration.

5 What is a refugee?

6 What is an economic migrant?

Changing Places!

Migration is the movement of people from one place to go to live in another. Emigrants leave a country. Immigrants enter a country. People migrate because of push and pull factors.

Push factors are the reasons that make someone decide to move. Often they are negative things such as unemployment, crop failure, drought, flooding, war, poor education opportunities or services and amenities. Pull factors are the things about the destination that attract people. They are usually positive things such as job opportunities or a better standard of living, better education, better healthcare. Migration can be classified in different groups:

¹_____ The movement of people to another country for a better standard of living. These people are often called economic migrants.

²_____ The movement of people from one region in a country to another is due to job opportunities, warmer weather or for higher salaries.

³_____ The movement of people from the countryside to the cities in countries where amenities and opportunities are greater in urban areas. This mainly happens in developing countries such as India.

⁴_____ The movement out of cities into rural areas for a more relaxed lifestyle and less pollution.

⁵_____ People who have to leave their homes or country due to war, political conflict or natural hazards such as floods.

2 READING & SPEAKING

a Read the article. In pairs, ask and answer the questions. Mark the sentences T (true), F (false), or DS (doesn't say). Correct the false sentences.

1 27% of the population of Greater London was born in the United Kingdom.

2 The first Italian immigrants lived in the Clerkenwell Road area of London.

3 The Italian Church in London was the second Italian Church to be built outside of Italy.

4 Some Italian immigrants in the 1800s sold ice-cream in London.

5 The Madonna del Carmine procession in London is in June.

b Underline five new words or phrases you want to learn from the text.

3 LISTENING & SPEAKING

a **25.1** Listen to Elisa Di Benedetto talking about why she immigrated to London. What were the push and pull factors that influenced her decision to leave Italy?

b **25.1** Listen again and circle the right answer.

1 She left Italy when she was 21 / 23.

2 She arrived in London 13th November 1957 / 30th November 1957.

3 She wanted to go to London to find a job / visit relatives.

4 She left Italy because there was no work / too much work.

5 She arrived in London at Paddington Station / Victoria Station.

6 She got a job as a nurse / teacher.

What do you think?
※ Would you like to live in London? Why (not)?
※ In developing countries people move from rural to urban areas. In developed countries people often move from the city to the country. Why?

LITTLE ITALY IN LONDON

London is one of the most multicultural cities in the world. Approximately 27% of the population of London were born outside the United Kingdom and more than 300 languages are spoken there. During the 19th and early 20th centuries one of the largest immigrant communities in central London was the Italian community. Many Italians immigrated there and settled in the area of London around Clerkenwell

Road. This area was called 'little Italy'. They mainly worked as organ-grinders, ice-cream sellers or as artisans making plaster statues, mirrors, and scientific instruments such as barometers. In 1846 St Peter's Church was built on Clerkenwell Road – the first Church for an Italian community to be built outside of Italy!

During the 1950s there was a new wave of Italian immigration to London. Italians came to London to escape unemployment in Italy and found jobs with regular salaries in factories, hospitals, and the building trade. The Italian community in London is now fully integrated and spread all over the city. Every year in July the Italian immigrants in London meet at St Peter's Italian church in Clerkenwell to take part in the celebration of the Madonna del Carmine and St Peter's Italian church continues to be a focal point for Italians in London, both young and old.

PROJECT

Write an article (100 words) for a school magazine about why people might want to immigrate to Italy. Include information on:
• where they come from
• what are the push factors
• what are the pull factors

UNITED IN DIVERSITY

1 _____

After World War II, European Governments wanted to form a United States of Europe, to help the people of Europe live in peace. In 1957 France, Italy, Belgium, the Netherlands, Luxembourg, and West Germany formed the European Economic Community (EEC). The United Kingdom joined this in 1973. The EEC changed its name to the European Union (EU) after the Maastricht Treaty in 1993.

2 _____

The European Union (EU) is a political body which has a single market, and common policies for trade, agriculture and fisheries between member states. Euro coins and banknotes have replaced national currencies in 13 of the member states. These countries are called the Euro Zone.

3 _____

European Union citizens can live, travel, and work in other member states (with some temporary restrictions on new member states). The Schengen Agreement abolished passport control and customs checks between some member states. Twenty three languages are spoken in the European Union. English is the most spoken foreign language followed by German and French.

4 _____

Important EU institutions and bodies include the European Commission, the Council of the European Union, the European Council, the European Central Bank, the European Court of Justice and the European Parliament. Citizens of EU member states are also EU citizens.

1 READING & SPEAKING

a How much do you know about the European Union?

b Do the European Union Quiz.

1 What is the European Union?

2 What is the most common language in the European Union?

3 What are the most important institutions of the European Union?

4 How many countries are in the Euro Zone?

5 What is the Euro Zone?

6 How often do elections to the European Parliament take place?

c Read the text and check your answers.

d Read the text and put these headings in the correct place.

The European Union today

The European Union Institutions

People of the European Union

History of the European Union

e Cover the text. Match the sentence halves a–d with 1–4.

a The European Union

b European Union citizens are able to

c The United Kingdom

d The European Economic Community became

1 the European Union (EU) following the Maastricht Treaty in 1993.

2 became a member of the European Union in 1973.

3 move freely and work in other member states.

4 is a political body.

2 LISTENING & READING

a **26.1** Listen to and read the information about the Institutions in the EU then answer the questions.

1 What is the European Commission?

2 Where is the European Parliament?

3 How often do European Elections take place?

4 What is the Euro Zone?

5 What is Europol?

d Cover the text. In pairs, can you remember what these numbers or dates refer to? Write a sentence using each number.

1993	1957	1973	13	5
1998	23	82%	2020	20%

3 LISTENING & SPEAKING

a **26.2** Read the five statements. Now listen to a member of the European Parliament saying what a country needs to join the European Union. Tick the three things he says.

To join the European Union a country must:

1 have the euro.

2 be a democracy.

3 have a good record of human rights.

4 have the death penalty.

5 follow European Union rules and regulations.

What do you think?

❉ The motto of the EU in Latin is *in variegate concordia* – 'united in diversity'.
What does this mean?

❉ How are EU countries different but united?

PROJECT

Write a short article (150 words) about the EU today. Use the Internet to help you. Include information on:
• which countries are members of the EU
• which countries have the Euro currency
• which countries are going to join shortly

The European Commission is the European Union's executive branch which means it is responsible for proposing new laws. It has a commissioner from each member state. The European Commission is based in Brussels.

The Council of the European Union is made up of one minister (responsible for the European Union law being proposed) from each member state. For example, a law regarding agriculture would be treated by a Council composed of the national ministers for agriculture from each member state. The presidency of the council changes between member states every six months.

The European Parliament is made up of representatives elected by the citizens of the European Union. Elections take place every five years. The European Parliament meets in Strasbourg and Luxembourg. The European parliament meets to discuss the legislation proposed by the European commission.

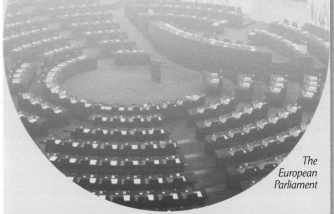

The European Parliament

The European Court of Justice is made up of judges from each member state. A president is elected from the judges. The European Court of Justice has the last word on Union law. European Union law is the first, and only, example of a supranational legal framework. Laws are only passed at European level when these are more effective compared to the legislation of the member states.

The European Central Bank (ECB) controls the monetary policy within the Euro Zone (the member states that adopted the Euro as their national currency). It was established in 1998 and it is based in Frankfurt, Germany.

Europol is the European Union instrument of law enforcement and fighting racism. This also includes the areas of illegal immigration and political asylum. It also helps provide criminal intelligence for member states.

Since the establishment of the European Union there have been no wars between its member countries!

Oskar Schindler

■ Schindler was born on 28 April 1908 in Moravia. When he left school he started various businesses. In 1939 Schindler joined the Nazi Party. He was one of the many businessmen who tried to profit from the German invasion of Poland in 1939. Schindler took possession of a factory in Krakow from a Jewish industrialist.

1 Oskar Schindler was a German industrialist who saved the lives of almost 1,100 Jews during the Holocaust. Schindler gave them jobs in his factories. Steven Spielberg made a film about Oskar Schindler's experiences during the war. The film won 7 Academy Awards.

■ At the end of the Second World War, Schindler had no money. He had spent all of his money on bribes and buying food on the black-market for his workers. Schindler was a very poor man and he lived with money from the Jews that he had helped. Schindler died at the age of 66 in Frankfurt, Germany in 1974. He is buried at the Catholic Cemetery at Mount Zion in Jerusalem.

■ The original list with the names of the Jews Schindler had saved called 'Schindler's List' was found in 1999 and is now in the Holocaust Museum of Yad Vashem in Israel.

■ Schindler needed people to work in his factory. He asked the Nazi's if he could have 1000 Jews to work for him. The names of these workers were on a piece of paper which the Jews called Schindler's list. These people were protected from the Nazi's and Schindler's accountant said 'the list means life'. During the 1942 raid on the Krakow Ghetto Schindler was horrified by the murder of many of the Jews who worked for him. Schindler began to protect his workers by bribing Nazi officials. Many of them were unskilled but he said they were still important for his factory.

■ In 1967, Schindler was honoured at Israel's Yad Vashem memorial as a "righteous among the nations", an honour by Israel to non-Jews who saved Jews during the Holocaust at great personal risk.

1 READING & SPEAKING

a In pairs, ask and answer the questions.

Have you seen the film Schindler's List?

Do you know what it is about?

b Read the text about Oskar Schindler and number the paragraphs in the right order 1–6.

c Read the text again in the right order. In pairs, ask and answer the questions.

1 Who was Oskar Schindler?

2 What was Schindler's list?

3 How did Schindler save the Jews?

4 What happened to Schindler after the war?

5 Where is Schindler's list now?

What do you think?

✷ Oskar Schindler and Giorgio Perlasca have both received the honour from Israel of the 'Righteous Among the Nations'. What do you think this means?

✷ After the war, Perlasca went back to Italy and didn't tell anyone what he had done. Why do you think this was?

2 LISTENING & SPEAKING

a In pairs, answer the question.

● Do you know any other war heroes?

● What do you know about Giorgio Perlasca?

b 27.1 Listen to the biography of Giorgio Perlasca and make some notes.

Giorgio Perlasca	
Hungary	
The Spanish Embassy	
The safe houses	
November 1944	
Safe conduct passes	
After the War	

c 27.1 Compare with a partner. Then listen again and complete your notes.

PROJECT

The 27th January is The Holocaust Memorial Day. On this day in 1945 the Soviet Army liberated the Nazi extermination camps at Auschwitz-Birkenau in Poland. Many schools in the UK mark the Holocaust Memorial Day by organizing different events.

Use the Internet to find out what other students in schools in Europe organize on this day. Write an article (150 words) for a school magazine about Holocaust Memorial Day. Include information on:

• what the Holocaust Memorial Day is

• what its aims are

• what young people in Europe do on this day

• what your school will do on this day

Audio CD track listing

The attached CD contains the audio material for the listening exercises in this book.

Listening	Track	Lesson	Page
T 1.1	1	Capitals of the UK	5
T 2.1	2	English around the world	6
T 2.2	3	English around the world	7
T 3.1	4	UK teenagers and their free time	8
T 4.1	5	Age limits in the UK	10
T 5.1	6	Road safety	12
T 6.1	7	Bullying	15
T 7.1	8	Education in the UK and USA	17
T 8.1	9	Festivals	18
T 8.2	10	Festivals	18
T 9.1	11	Superstitions in the UK and USA	20
T 10.1	12	Young people and work	23
T 11.1	13	University and gap years	24
T 12.1	14	Summer camps	26
T 13.1	15	MTV	29
T 14.1	16	Shopping streets	31
T 15.1	17	Transport in London	32
T 16.1	18	Wonders of the world	34
T 16.2	19	Wonders of the world	35
T 17.1	20	History of Art – Art in the UK	37
T 18.1	21	Earth Sciences – Pollution and aviation	39
T 19.1	22	Literature – the novel: Love and Marriage	40
T 19.2	23	Literature – the novel: Love and Marriage	41
T 20.1	24	History – The textile industry and the Industrial Revolution	43
T 21.1	25	Geography – Tourism	45
T 22.1	26	Physics – Great inventors	46
T 23.1	27	Biology – Diet and the food pyramid	48
T 24.1	28	Earth Sciences – Rubbish and recycling	50
T 25.1	29	Geography – Migration	53
T 26.1	30	Politics – The European Union	55
T 26.2	31	Politics – The European Union	55
T 27.1	32	History – True heroes of war	57

DVD Contents

DVD

Each section has five parts:

- The interview (part 1 and part 2)
- Common words and phrases from The interview
- In the street
- Common words and phrases from In the street

THE INTERVIEW

a You're going to watch an interview with Charles Collingwood, a British actor who has worked in the theatre, on TV, and on radio. He is most famous for his role in *The Archers*, a radio soap opera about a family of farmers, which has been broadcast every day on BBC radio since 1951 and is the longest running radio serial in the world. Before you listen, read the glossary and look at how the words are pronounced to help you understand what he says.

> **Glossary**
>
> **RADA** The Royal Academy of Dramatic Art, a college where people train to become actors
> **learn your lines** to memorize the words you have to say
> **props** *n* /prɒps/ small objects used by actors during a play or in a film
> **rehearse** *v* /rɪ'hɜːs/ to practise for a performance or recording
> **ad-lib** *v* /æd 'lɪb/ to say something in a play that is not in your script, to improvise
> **producers' gallery** place in a studio where the producer and technicians sit
> **stale** *adj* /steɪl/ hard, not fresh, e.g. cake

b **1.1** Listen to part 1. Mark the statements T (true) or F (false).
1 He enjoys radio more than TV because he feels very relaxed doing it.
2 As a young actor he thought he would be a TV or film actor.
3 He is pleased to have spent half his life doing the same soap opera.
4 The first advantage he mentions of being a radio actor is that you don't need to dress well.
5 TV soap operas have longer scenes than radio soap operas.
6 Radio actors have to rehearse a scene many times.

c **1.2** Listen to part 2. Answer the questions with a partner.
1 Why do actors sometimes get a nasty surprise when the envelope with the latest script arrives?
2 What example does Charles give of how he sometimes changes the script?
3 What does he try *not* to sound like when he plays his character?
4 Which two examples does he give of sound effects which the actors do themselves now?
5 When Charles first worked on *The Archers* how did he do the sound effect for kissing?
6 Why was the woman in the supermarket so surprised when Charles interrupted her conversation with her son?

d **1.3** Listen and complete the phrases with one or two words. What do you think they mean?

> **COMMON WORDS AND PHRASES**
> 1 I'm able to just _____ myself into it and enjoy every moment.
> 2 I of course thought I'd have a life in the theatre, but it didn't _____ out that way…
> 3 Television acting _____ a very long _____…
> 4 … you rehearse once, possibly twice and then you record it, and then you _____ _____…
> 5 What we don't know in _____ before the scripts arrive is to what's happening to your character.

e Listen to the interview again with the tapescript on page 67. Would you prefer to be a radio or TV actor? Why?

IN THE STREET

a **1.4** You're going to watch five people talking about listening to the radio. Listen once and complete the *Where…?* column.

| | Steve | Sarah | Nick | Jane | Elke |

	Where do you listen to the radio?	What do you listen to?
Steve		
Sarah		
Nick		
Jane		
Elke		

b Listen again. Complete the *What…?* column.

c **1.5** Listen and complete the phrases. What do you think they mean?

> **COMMON WORDS AND PHRASES**
> 1 _____ in the car, when I'm driving…
> 2 …my housemate listens to the radio in the morning, and when she puts it on I listen to it _____ _____.
> 3 …often the news and just debates and that _____ of _____.
> 4 Yes, I listen to the radio _____ _____ when I'm driving to work.
> 5 I drive to work in the car and it takes _____ a long _____…
> 6 …it takes an hour _____ _____…

d Listen to the interviews again with the tapescript on page 67. Then ask and answer the same questions with a partner.

THE INTERVIEW

a You're going to watch an interview with Jeanette Hughes, who works for a local council as Health Development Officer. She gives advice and practical help to encourage people to do more exercise, eat healthily, and stop smoking. Before you listen, read the glossary and look at how the words are pronounced to help you understand what she says.

> ### Glossary
>
> **calories** /'kæləriz/ units for measuring how much energy food will produce
>
> **hockey** /'hɒki/ a team sport played on grass or on ice where you hit a ball with a stick
>
> **netball** /'netbɔːl/ a team sport similar to basketball usually played by women
>
> **skateboarding** /'skeɪtbɔːdɪŋ/ a sport where you stand on and ride a board with small wheels
>
> **household** n /'haʊshəʊld/ all the people living together in a house
>
> **nutrition** /nju'trɪʃn/ the food that you eat and the way that it affects your health
>
> **legislation** /ledʒɪs'leɪʃn/ a law or group of laws

b **2.1** Listen to part 1. Answer the questions with a partner.
1 What's the first reason she gives for why people do less exercise? What examples does she give?
2 How many calories did a housewife in the 1950s use doing the weekly housework?
3 What other reason does she give for people doing less exercise?
4 What changes have there been in the kind of sports children do at school? Why?
5 What difference does she mention between girls and boys doing exercise?

c **2.2** Listen to part 2. Mark the statements T (true) or F (false).
1 She says that young people eat more healthily than older people.
2 Older people cook vegetables in an unhealthy way.
3 Young people eat more vegetables than older people.
4 In 2006 the number of smokers in Britain had gone down by 17%.
5 People are smoking less because of the changes in legislation.
6 Smokers are happy to have a cigarette outside in the street.
7 It's only older people who want help to stop smoking.
8 Some parents come to ask for help to stop their children from smoking.

d **2.3** Listen and complete the phrases with one or two words. What do you think they mean?

COMMON WORDS AND PHRASES
1 Young people while they're at school, they're still doing an _____ lot of activity.
2 …they're more likely to _____ _____ when they've finished school.
3 I think the _____ _____ would generally eat more vegetables…
4 Whereas people felt it was OK to smoke _____…
5 …they just don't want to go out and get _____ wet and _____ cold…
6 It's not as _____ as it was, people understand the dangers now…

e Listen to the interview again with the tapescript on page 67. Is what she says about exercise, diet, and smoking similar in your region?

IN THE STREET

a **2.4** You're going to watch five people talking about how fit they are. Listen once. Who do you think is probably the fittest?

1	2	3	4	5
Jade	Nadia	Nick	Sarah	Geri

b Listen again. Who...?
A cycles and is learning to dance ☐
B does exercise in a gym ☐
C is fit because he / she dances ☐ ☐
D doesn't do anything to keep fit ☐
E does exercise twice a week ☐

c **2.5** Listen and complete the phrases. What do you think they mean?

COMMON WORDS AND PHRASES
1 I exercise a couple of times a week, so _____ fit I think.
2 I go to the gym _____…
3 I'm probably _____ fit.
4 …and I also take dance classes, which is _____ _____.
5 Nothing _____ _____.

d Listen to the interviews again with the tapescript on page 68. Then ask and answer the same questions with a partner.

THE INTERVIEW

a You're going to watch an interview with Cos Antoniou, a driving instructor. Before you listen, read the glossary and look at how the words are pronounced to help you understand what he says.

> **Glossary**
>
> **manoeuvres** *n* /mə'nuːvəz/ movements in a car that have to be done carefully and correctly, e.g. parking
>
> **reversing** /rɪ'vɜːsɪŋ/ going backwards
>
> **speed** /spiːd/ how fast something is moving, e.g. a speed limit, a speed camera
>
> **insurance** /ɪn'ʃʊərəns/ money you pay to a company. If you have an accident, the company pays to repair your car.
>
> **stationary** *adj* /'steɪʃənri/ not moving
>
> **a zebra crossing** /zebrə 'krɒsɪŋ/ an area of road marked with black and white lines where people can cross the road
>
> **the passenger seat** /pæsɪndʒə(r) siːt/ the seat next to the driver's seat

b **3.1** Listen to part 1. Answer the questions with a partner.
1 How long has he been teaching people to drive?
2 Why does he say a driving instructor has to be 'a type of chameleon'?
3 What other qualities does a driving instructor need?
4 How many times do most people take the driving test before they pass?
5 Does he think the British driving test should be made easier or more difficult?

c **3.2** Listen to part 2. Answer the questions with a partner.
What does he say about...?
1 the difference between men and women drivers
2 boys' attitude to driving after they pass their test
3 why insurance is cheaper for women
4 when accidents can happen during a driving lesson
5 an accident he had
6 a change he would make to the law
7 driving in his free time

d **3.3** Listen and complete the phrases with one or two words. What do you think they mean?

COMMON WORDS AND PHRASES

1 I think it goes _____ _____ that we have to be patient, and you have to be a people type of person.
2 ...it can be very stressful _____ _____ who you're teaching...
3 ...it's the car behind that doesn't stop and ends up in the back of them, and that's what _____ _____ me once.
4 _____ _____ I think they do make better, safer drivers than men.
5 ...they do not keep their speed down to a reasonable level, _____ women tend to drive the way they're taught...

e Listen to the interview again with the tapescript on page 68. Do you agree with what he says about men and women drivers?

IN THE STREET

a **3.4** You're going to watch five people talking about learning to drive. How many of them passed their test the first time?

| 1 Elke | 2 Steve | 3 Jane | 4 Nicholas | 5 Blanca |

b Listen again. Who...?
A thinks that his / her driving has improved ☐ ☐
B thinks he / she needs to have more driving lessons ☐
C was taught mainly by a member of their family ☐
D feels much more confident than he / she used to ☐
E says he / she has problems driving in the UK ☐

c **3.5** Listen and complete the phrases. What do you think they mean?

COMMON WORDS AND PHRASES

1 Yes, I did, I am _____ to say.
2 Driving lessons _____ years _____.
3 I had _____ _____ lessons with my father...
4 _____ my father but I had some lessons as well.
5 I had to take quite a lot of lessons because I wasn't very _____ _____ _____.

d Listen to the interviews again with the tapescript on page 68. Then ask and answer the same questions with a partner.

THE INTERVIEW

a You're going to watch an interview with Ingrid Roe, who works in a small clothes shop in New York. Before you listen, read the glossary and look at how the words are pronounced to help you understand what she says.

> ### Glossary
>
> **suit** *v* /suːt/ to look attractive in sth, e.g. *that dress really suits you*
> **go with sth** (*idiom*) /gəʊ wɪð/ to match or look good with sth
> **wardrobe** *n* /ˈwɔːdrəʊb/ a large cupboard where people keep clothes
> **a sale** /seɪl/ noun from the verb *sell*
> **a return** *n* /rɪˈtɜːn/ sth that is taken back to a shop by a customer
> **a store** *n* /stɔː(r)/ (especially in North American English) a shop
> **stand in as proxy** /stænd ɪn əz ˈprɒksi/ take sb's place
> **shoplifting** *v* /ˈʃɒplɪftɪŋ/ stealing things from a shop
> **merchant** *n* /ˈmɜːtʃənt/ (especially in North American English) a shop owner
> **dry-cleaning** *n* /ˌdraɪ ˈkliːnɪŋ/ a method of cleaning clothes with chemicals

b **4.1** Listen to part 1. Mark the statements T (true) or F (false).
1 The typical customer in her shop is a young single woman.
2 In general her customers know what they want.
3 Ingrid thinks the best way to help a customer is by asking them the right questions.
4 The most difficult customers are the ones who don't know what they want.
5 Ingrid doesn't always tell her customers the truth because she doesn't want to hurt their feelings.

c **4.2** Listen to part 2. Answer the questions with a partner.
1 What men come to her shop?
2 Why are some men easier than others?
3 What do the shop assistants sometimes have to do to help male customers?
4 Why isn't shoplifting a big problem in her shop?
5 What do shop owners do to help each other?
6 What does she mean by…?
   a 'a sense of belonging'
   b 'feeling a little bit locked in sometimes'

d **4.3** Listen and complete the phrases with one or two words. What do you think they mean?

> ### COMMON WORDS AND PHRASES
> 1 …a woman who has different things _____ _____ in her life…
> 2 …in general they know what they're shopping for in _____ of a certain event or a special occasion.
> 3 Someone who isn't listening to what you're saying, who asks _____ after _____…
> 4 I don't want someone to go home with something for _____ _____ of a sale…
> 5 …we have a very _____ _____ with our customers…

e Listen to the interview again with the tapescript on page 68. Do you think Ingrid is probably a good shop assistant? Why (not)?

IN THE STREET

a **4.4** You're going to watch five people talking about shopping in clothes shops. Which two speakers sometimes like to be helped by shop assistants?

1	2	3	4	5
Nick	Mercedes	Geri	Nadia	Joey

b Listen again. Tick five things they mention that irritate them about shop assistants.
when they are not polite ☐
when they don't help you ☐
when they don't know about what they're selling ☐
when they take a long time to serve you ☐
when they tell you that you look really good in something ☐
when they try to convince you to buy something very expensive ☐
when they try to get you to buy something you don't want ☐

c **4.5** Listen and complete the phrases. What do you think they mean?

> ### COMMON WORDS AND PHRASES
> 1 …but quite often I can _____ _____ quite irritating.
> 2 I like to _____ myself because I know what I like.
> 3 They always try to convince you that something that you are looking at is fantastic _____ _____.
> 4 When they're rude, when they don't really want to, like, _____ _____ _____.
> 5 If I'm looking for a particular thing; if I'm not, I like to just shop, kind of, _____ _____.

d Listen to the interviews again with the tapescript on page 68. Then ask and answer the same questions with a partner.

THE INTERVIEW

a You're going to watch an interview with Camilla Naprous, who is a stunt rider, and trains horses and actors for films. Before you listen, read the glossary and look at how the words are pronounced to help you understand what she says.

> **Glossary**
>
> **stunt** *n* /stʌnt/ a dangerous and difficult action a person does, especially as part of a film
>
> **gallop** *v* /ˈɡæləp/ to ride a horse very fast
>
> **battlefield** *n* /ˈbætlfiːld/ the place where a battle is fought
>
> **production** *n* /prəˈdʌkʃn/ the producer(s) of a film who deal with the practical and business side of making a film
>
> **double** *n* /ˈdʌbl/ a person who replaces another actor in a film to do dangerous or other special things
>
> **movie** *n* /ˈmuːvi/ (especially in North American English) a film
>
> *The Other Boleyn Girl* a 2008 historical film starring Natalie Portman and Scarlett Johansson
>
> *The Horse Whisperer* a 1998 film starring Robert Redford about a man who works with horses
>
> *Season of the Witch* a 2010 US thriller starring Nicolas Cage

b ▪5.1▪ Listen to part 1. Answer the questions with a partner.
1 How old was she when she learnt to ride? Who taught her?
2 What kind of stunt is a 'Roman ride'? Is it dangerous?
3 Was her father worried about her?
4 Why do the horses she trains have to be brave?
5 What kind of horses does she mainly work with?
6 How long does she have to teach actors to ride?

c ▪5.2▪ Listen to part 2. Mark the statements T (true) or F (false).
1 Men are easier to teach than women.
2 In films most of the riding is done by doubles.
3 Natalie Portman and Scarlett Johansson both became very good riders.
4 Natalie had more experience than Scarlett.
5 Camilla worked with them for two months.
6 She enjoyed working on *Season of the Witch* because Nicholas Cage was in it.

d ▪5.3▪ Listen and complete the phrases with one or two words. What do you think they mean?

> **COMMON WORDS AND PHRASES**
> 1 It's best to start from an early _____ really because you have no fear.
> 2 _____ wood, not yet.
> 3 _____ of the time we have to teach them.
> 4 It all _____ _____ what time period they have.
> 5 Some directors want their actors to ride _____-_____.
> 6 It's _____ to be between Natalie Portman and Scarlett Johansson.

e Listen to the interview again with the tapescript on page 69. Have you ever been riding? Would you like to be taught by Camilla?

IN THE STREET

a ▪5.4▪ You're going to watch five people talking about animal cartoons and working with animals. Which cartoon is mentioned twice? Who wouldn't mind working with animals?

Daphne   **Jade**   **Ash**   **Elke**   **Ashley**

b Listen again. Who…?
A says he / she likes one animal in particular ☐
B cried when they first saw their favourite animal film ☐
C has a health problem related to animals ☐
D thought their favourite film was a perfect family film ☐
E liked a film because he / she had seen the same animals in the wild ☐

c ▪5.5▪ Listen and complete the phrases. What do you think they mean?

> **COMMON WORDS AND PHRASES**
> 1 I don't like every animal, I guess, and looking at them _____ a _____ is enough.
> 2 I like dogs, but as a _____ , probably not.
> 3 Because they're _____ _____ _____ and noisy.
> 4 It's really funny and it _____ _____ for both adults and children…
> 5 I mean the first thing that _____ to mind is a vet…

d Listen to the interviews again with the tapescript on page 69. Then ask and answer the same questions with a partner.

THE INTERVIEW

a You're going to watch an interview with Bob Fenton, a retired police detective. Before you listen, read the glossary and look at how the words are pronounced to help you understand what he says.

Glossary

break into /breɪk ˈɪntə/ to enter a building by force
magistrate *n* /ˈmædʒɪstreɪt/ a judge who deals with less serious crime
custodial order *n* /kʌˈstəʊdɪəl ˈɔːdə(r)/ a prison sentence
play the system /pleɪ ðə ˈsɪstəm/ to get what <u>you</u> want from a system (here the criminal justice system)
armed *adj* /ɑːmd/ carrying a weapon, e.g. a gun
bullets /ˈbʊlɪts/ small pieces of metal that are fired from a gun
give yourself up /gɪv jɔːˈself ʌp/ allow yourself to be arrested
gallantry medal /ˈgæləntri ˈmedl/ a medal given to someone for a brave action

b **6.1** Listen to part 1. Answer the questions with a partner.
1 Do criminals usually confess to their crimes?
2 What part of the body does he mention that helps you know if someone is lying?
3 Who is better at lying, men or women?
4 What excuse did the burglar give?
5 Does he think community service is a good punishment?

c **6.2** Listen to part 2. Mark the statements T (true) or F (false).
1 The most dangerous situation in which he was involved was going after some criminals in a car.
2 The criminals abandoned their car in the middle of the road.
3 The criminals fired five bullets into the police car.
4 Finally, the men were arrested and given short prison sentences.
5 The detective was given a medal by a member of the Royal Family.
6 Police officers often end up getting divorced because they spend so little time with their partners.
7 His daughters are all police officers.
8 Two of them are also married to police officers.

d **6.3** Listen and complete the phrases with one or two words. What do you think they mean?

COMMON WORDS AND PHRASES
1 The problem is that _____ of the _____ they're interviewed by men…
2 Community service is a _____ _____ in my opinion.
3 …a lot of them will go back to crime _____ _____…
4 …they _____ came out after a few days…
5 …they all _____ _____ be girls…

e Listen to the interview again with the tapescript on page 69. How would you describe Bob Fenton's attitude to criminals? Does he make being a detective sound like an attractive job?

IN THE STREET

a **6.4** You're going to watch five people talking about their favourite fictional detectives and crimes they have witnessed. Tick the six detectives they mention.
Columbo ☐ Inspector Clouseau ☐ Inspector Morse ☐
Inspector Wallander ☐ Miss Marple ☐ Nancy Drew ☐
Poirot ☐ Sherlock Holmes ☐

Steve   Sarah   Ashley   Elke   Francesco

b Listen again. Who…?
A has seen someone stealing from a shop ☐☐
B saw a vehicle being stolen ☐
C has never witnessed a crime ☐☐
D likes a detective because of someone in his / her family ☐
E enjoyed both the books and films about a detective ☐
F likes the physical appearance of a detective ☐
G enjoys how a detective solves the crimes ☐☐

c **6.5** Listen and complete the phrases. What do you think they mean?

COMMON WORDS AND PHRASES
1 …but he actually does solve them _____ _____ _____.
2 I _____ so, yeah.
3 I've seen people shoplifting and then _____ _____ from the store.
4 …all the stories _____ _____ in Oxford and that's where I live, so it's very interesting.
5 No, _____ not, no.

d Listen to the interviews again with the tapescript on page 70. Then ask and answer the same questions with a partner.

THE INTERVIEW

a You're going to watch an interview with Sandy Kaiser, a diplomat who works at the American Embassy in London. Before you listen, read the glossary and look at how the words are pronounced to help you understand what she says.

Glossary

consulate *n* /'kɒnsjələt/ similar to an embassy but not in a capital city

Serbo-Croatian /sɜːbəʊ krəʊ'eɪʃn/ the language spoken by people from Croatia, Serbia, Montenegro, and Bosnia

the Rhineland /'raɪnlænd/ the land on both sides of the river Rhine, in the west of Germany

pharmacy /'fɑːməsi/ (especially in North American English) chemist's

grocery store /'ɡrəʊsəri stɔː(r)/ (especially in North American English) a shop selling groceries, e.g. flour, sugar, tea, and coffee

---

b **7.1** Listen to part 1. Answer the questions with a partner.
1 What was the first country she worked in? Did she learn the language?
2 What was one of the best moments of her stay?
3 Which country did she nearly go to next? Why didn't she go there?
4 Which country did she go to instead? How well did she learn the language?
5 Which three European countries did she go to after that? Which language did she study?

c **7.2** Listen to part 2. What does she say about...?
1 how long she's been in London and what she thinks of it
2 what President Obama said about the relationship between the UK and the US
3 the British village
4 big open vistas
5 the cost of living in the UK and the US
6 why British people are surprised when they go to the US

d **7.3** Listen and complete the phrases with one or two words. What do you think they mean?

COMMON WORDS AND PHRASES

1 ...and then I was _____ _____ to go to Rio de Janeiro...
2 ...it was one of the _____ _____, I think, of my diplomatic career...
3 After that I was _____ my _____ to the former Yugoslavia, to Sarajevo...
4 Instead I _____ up going to Estonia...
5 I did not have to study Danish, although I did _____ _____ a few phrases...
6 One big thing that _____ me in terms of difference is...

e Listen to the interview again with the tapescript on page 70. What do you think are the pros and cons of being a diplomat?

IN THE STREET

a **7.4** You're going to watch four people talking about whether they find British English or American English easier to understand and where they would prefer to live, the UK or the US. How many people...?
a find US English easier to understand
b would prefer to live in the UK

Elke   José   Francesco   Daniela

b Listen again. Who...?
A learnt a lot of English from films and TV ☐
B learnt British English at school ☐☐
C has lived in both the UK and the US ☐
D prefers the weather in the US ☐☐
E thinks that British people speak more slowly and clearly than American people ☐☐

c **7.5** Listen and complete the phrases. What do you think they mean?

COMMON WORDS AND PHRASES

1 And any English or American films we saw would always be _____...
2 ...you don't really get a _____ to hear much of American English.
3 I couldn't _____ _____ living in America now for that reason.
4 ...lots of people from _____ in the world.
5 I _____ _____ at the moment the US.

d Listen to the interviews again with the tapescript on page 70. Then ask and answer the same questions with a partner.

Listening

1.1 **Interviewer** You have worked in theatre, TV and radio. Which do you most enjoy?

Charles Collingwood Now, I enjoy radio most because it's the medium I've spent so long in, so I'm so familiar with it that I can relax, it doesn't make me nervous, I'm able to just throw myself into it and enjoy every moment. As a young actor, theatre was what I enjoyed most. All actors, I think, become actors to work in theatre, that's what you set out to do and when I left RADA in, when I was a young man aged 21 or 2 in 1963, I of course thought I'd have a life in the theatre, but it didn't work out that way, I've spent over half my life in the longest running soap opera in the world and I'm jolly proud of it.

I What advantage does radio acting have over TV acting?

C I think many. The obvious answer is that we don't have to learn our lines, because nobody can see us. It's quite interesting if you watch a television soap, very few scenes will last longer than two minutes, because the actors have got to learn the lines, and there is only so many words an actor can get into his head before recording; we don't have that problem at all. The more artistic thing for me, the thing that I get from it as an actor, is its immediacy. Television acting takes a very long time – setting it up, getting the lighting, the sound – everything has to be exactly in order, and then you do the scene, and something goes wrong, one of the props doesn't work, or somebody makes a noise or an aircraft flies over, or a car goes by, you know, you don't know what's going to happen. The joy of radio is that you turn up, you read it through with the other actors, you go in the studio, you rehearse once, possibly twice and then you record it, and then you move on, so I love the immediacy of radio.

1.2 **I** Do you get your script before you go to the studio to record the programme?

C Well, we do get them in advance, correct. What we don't know in advance before the scripts arrive is to what's happening to your character. There have been occasions in the past when actors have opened their envelope of scripts and to their horror found that they've gone under a tractor or hit a tree or something like that, and that's not much fun for them.

I Do you follow the script strictly or do you ad-lib sometimes?

C I follow the script 90%. If the line is 'Are you coming to see us tonight?' and the reply is 'We'll be there are six.', I might just go 'Yeah, yeah, I'll be there at six.' just to make it more conversational. I also try not to sound too much like an actor. Actors, because we've been trained, tend to have good voices and good speech, good projection, while the public don't, so I don't play my character as deliberately as I am talking to you.

I How are the sound effects done in radio drama?

C Well, a great many of them are played in by the technicians from the producers' gallery and they're on CD or disk or whatever it is, but we still do quite a lot ourselves. I mean, if we are required to walk, we walk and you hear our footsteps; if we eat, we eat – we don't eat anything very nice, you know, if it's a full Sunday roast, it's probably a rather stale piece of cake. When I first joined, if you had a love scene, and I'm delighted to say my character has had many love scenes, when you kissed the character, when they heard kissing, all it was was kissing the back of your hand, so I would go 'oh darling, mmm' like that, kiss the back of my hand, which is quite sad really; well gladly that's now stopped…

I Do you ever get recognized by your voice?

C Amazingly, more often than you'd believe, quite extraordinary. I was in a supermarket not long ago, and I overheard a woman with her child saying to her little boy – he was 11 or 12 – 'Now, concentrate. I'm going to drop you home before I go out to play tennis, but make sure when you get home that you don't forget to record *The Archers* at 7 o'clock, all right?' And I just jumped in between the two of them and said, 'Do as your mother's told', she nearly had a fit this woman, because she immediately recognized my voice and that was very funny.

1.4 **Interviewer** Do you listen to the radio?

Steve Yes.

I When and where do you listen to the radio?

S Mainly in the car when I'm driving or sometimes at home in quiet moments.

I What kind of programmes do you listen to?

S Generally listen to Radio 2, which is generally sort of music and comments about the world.

Interviewer Do you listen to the radio?

Sarah I do sometimes because my housemate listens to the radio in the morning and when she puts it on I listen to it as well.

I What kind of programmes do you listen to?

S It's usually Radio 4 and often the news and just debates and that kind of thing.

Interviewer Do you listen to the radio?

Nick Yes, I do.

I When and where do you listen to the radio?

N On the computer, on the Internet, and just in my bedroom.

I What kind of programmes do you listen to?

N 50s rock and contemporary music.

Interviewer Do you listen to the radio?

Jane Yes, I listen to the radio most mornings when I'm driving to work. I have a journey of about 40 minutes to take me to my work, so I listen to the radio then.

I What kind of programmes do you listen to?

J I often listen to Radio 2, I like the quiz programme in the morning. I listen to it coming home from work and I listen to the news programmes, I like the classical programmes, and I like Radio 4.

Interviewer Do you listen to the radio?

Elke Yes, I do, I really like listening to the radio.

I When and where do you listen to the radio?

E Usually in the mornings in the car. I drive to work in the car and it takes quite a long time, it takes an hour at least, and I always listen to the radio then.

I What kind of programmes do you listen to?

E In the mornings it's *The Today Programme*, which is all about politics and then sometimes I listen to music, whatever is on.

2.1 **Interviewer** Do you think people today do less exercise than in the past?

Jeanette Hughes I think on the whole, generally yes, there are a lot of people that will still do a fair amount of exercise and sport, but I think generally as a nation we do do less exercise.

I Why do you think that is?

J Technology is probably the primary reason – you've only got to look around your house: washing machine, vacuum cleaner,… we've even got something to turn the television over, haven't we? And I… and I read an interesting piece, a woman in the 1950s doing her housework in a week would have used the same amount of calories as it would take to run a marathon. So that… that's sort of the general daily activity we would have had in the 1950s that isn't there now because of technology.

I Anything else?

J Cars, I think, most people are using their cars far more than they were. So there's a whole heap of reasons on why people just generally in their daily lifestyle aren't as active as they were, so they're going to have to now look for different reasons to become active, whereas before it was just natural in your daily life.

I How about young people?

J Young people while they're at school, they're still doing an awful lot of activity. I think there have been government recommendations about how much activity there should be in school, and they are doing more and more. Whereas at one time they would have done hockey, football, netball, traditional sports, they're looking at other things that children and young people enjoy, so they're doing skateboarding, they're doing different types of water sport. By finding other activities that they can do which are more pleasurable for them, they're more likely to carry on when they've finished school.

I Is there a difference between girls and boys?

J Yeah, generally boys are more active, certainly at school, anyway, they definitely do more physical activity or more sports than the girls do.

2.2 **I** Do you think young people eat more healthily than the older generation?

J Ooh, that's a really kind of difficult one to say, I think it would be mixed in different households. I think the older generation, and this is generalizing, but I think the older generation would generally eat more vegetables. However, a lot of people will boil those vegetables for a long time and they will add salt, which isn't necessarily the best way to cook the vegetables and you won't necessarily have the same amount of vitamins, whereas the younger person might eat less but it might be cooked without salt and less boiling, so although they're having less they might be getting more nutrition, so it's a bit of a difficult one to say really.

I Is it true that the number of people who smoke has gone down in recent years?

J Yes, it is. In 1980 there was about 39% prevalence in smoking, in 2006 that had gone down to 22%, so there has been a steady decline in the smoking rates in this country.

I Why do you think that is?

J Lots and lots of different reasons. I think the change in legislation about smoking in closed public places changed a lot about perception. Whereas people felt it was OK to smoke anywhere, they're now realizing actually this isn't necessarily OK, so people have sometimes changed their minds because of the legislation. And now because they just don't want to go out and get soaking wet and freezing cold standing outside the pub having a cigarette, so I think, yeah, there's lots of different reasons. It's not as cool as it was, people understand the dangers now, I think a lot of the older smokers now wouldn't have known of the dangers when they took up smoking, it wasn't so widely known, whereas now I think it is, so there are less people starting as well as people giving up.

I What kind of people come to you for help to stop smoking?

J We get quite a mix actually, we get smokers and we also get non-smokers. The smokers will be from across the range, sometimes we do get quite young people coming in, saying well actually they started smoking thinking it was something they could put down relatively easy and were surprised how quick they got addicted. We also get quite a lot of young people coming in who don't smoke but are concerned about their parents and they come and ask advice about how to persuade their parents to give up smoking.

2.4 **Interviewer** How fit are you?
Jade I exercise a couple of times a week, so fairly fit I think.
Interviewer How fit are you?
Nadia Fairly fit, I like to cycle, I go to the gym occasionally, do yoga and the treadmill.
Interviewer How fit are you?
Nick Fairly fit, fairly fit.
I What do you do to keep fit?
N Mainly dancing.
Interviewer How fit are you?
Sarah I'm probably reasonably fit.
I What do you do to keep fit?
S I cycle a lot because I live outside of the centre so I have to cycle in every day and I also take dance classes, which is really fun.
Interviewer How fit are you?
Geri Not that fit, I must say.
I What do you do to keep fit?
G Nothing at all.

3.1 **Interviewer** How long have you been doing the job?
Cos Antoniou I've been a driving instructor now for some 33 years now.
I What kind of person do you need to be to be a driving instructor?
C I think a driving instructor needs to be a type of chameleon, he needs to change his style of teaching to suit the person that's sitting next to him. I think it goes without saying that we have to be patient, and you have to be a people type of person. You need to be able to react quickly to situations and you need to be able to give confidence to the person that is sitting next to you.
I Is it a very stressful job?
C Yes, it can be very stressful depending on who you're teaching and where you're teaching, but I enjoy it.
I Have you ever had an accident or near accident during a driving lesson?
C It's very rare for an instructor to have an accident on a driving lesson, but when we do have an accident on a driving lesson it's normally because we are stationary and it's the car behind that doesn't stop and ends up in the back of them. And that's what happened to me once. I was stationary at a zebra crossing, where people were crossing, and the car behind me did not stop and ended up in the back of our car.
I Do most people pass the test the first time?
C Most people don't really pass the first time, no.
I In your driving school what is the record for the most number of tests that someone has taken?
C With me the maximum amount of tests someone has taken is eight tests, but I've… I have heard that other driving schools have taken at least 25 tests. The maximum normally with me is about two.
I Do you think the driving test should be made more difficult?
C I think the driving test is as hard as it can be. The British driving test now is perhaps the hardest test, driving test, in the world. I don't think it should be made more difficult, but what I do feel that we can do to make it easier for people taking it is to split it up. We have the manoeuvres, that is turning in the road, reversing round the corner, and the reverse parking manoeuvres; if we can separate these from the actual drive, then we can make the test easier at the same time keeping it at a high level.

3.2 **I** In general do you think women make better drivers than men?

C In general I think they do make better, safer drivers than men. When men, or young boys, pass their driving test they tend to change their attitude to driving once they're on the road. They do not follow the way they're taught, they do not keep their speed down to a reasonable level, whereas women tend to drive the way they're taught and this is why insurance is cheaper for a woman than it is for a man.
I What one change would you make to the law to reduce accidents?
C I would make teaching driving compulsory in all schools so that you start teaching attitude and start teaching learning to drive in classroom first, and then having to then teach it on the road, I would make it compulsory to learn driving in classes.
I Do you enjoy driving in your free time?
C Yes, I do enjoy driving in my free time. It's the only time I get to drive, normally I'm in the passenger seat teaching someone how to drive and I really enjoy driving in Europe.

3.4 **Interviewer** How did you learn to drive?
Elke I learnt to drive when I was 18 in Germany and I took lessons, which took several weeks.
I Did you pass your test the first time?
E Yes, I did, I am proud to say.
I Do you think you're a good driver?
E I'm OK, I do have to do a bit of thinking when I drive in England and then again when I drive in Germany to make sure I drive on the right side and I do the right things, but yeah, I'm OK, I've not had any big accidents.
Interviewer How did you learn to drive?
Steve Driving lessons many years ago.
I Did you pass your test the first time?
S No.
I Do you think you're a good driver?
S Better than I was when I was younger.
Interviewer How did you learn to drive?
Jane I learnt to drive when I was 17, I had a few lessons with my father but mainly I had lessons with the driving instructor.
I Did you pass your test the first time?
J I did pass my test the first time, although it took me quite a many lessons before I was confident.
I Do you think you're a good driver?
J I think I'm a good driver, I've been driving for a long long time and I've never had any accidents or any convictions.
Interviewer How did you learn to drive?
Nicholas Mostly my father but I had some lessons as well.
I Did you pass your test the first time?
N No, third.
I Do you think you're a good driver?
N OK, but I've got a lot of experience now, so I'm OK.
Interviewer How did you learn to drive?
Blanca I learnt to drive when I was 18. I really wanted to have a driving licence, so as soon as I turned 18 I decided to take lessons and I had to take quite a lot of lessons because I wasn't very good at it. So I took something like 30 lessons and then I went for my exams.
I Did you pass your test the first time?
B No, I had to take my exams three times.
I Do you think you're a good driver?
B Well, the truth is, I haven't actually driven much since I passed my exam, so I think I'll need to take lessons again now if I want to start driving again.

4.1 **Interviewer** How would you describe your typical customer?
Ingrid Roe She's older, usually in mid-career woman, a woman who has different things going on in her life and who is usually part of a family and the women who come and really look for something that suits a lifestyle.

I Do they usually know what they want?
IR They do and they don't. It's like with every shopper, you sort of have your eye out for surprises, but in general they know what they're shopping for in terms of a certain event or a special occasion.
I And how do you help them choose what they want?
IR I listen to their needs. I essentially ask them if there is something specific that they needed to find, if it needs to go with something that they already own in their wardrobe and sort of that's a starting point and it's very easy to come up with a good solution, that is long lasting as well.
I What kind of customer do you find most difficult?
IR Someone who isn't listening to what you're saying, who asks question after question and doesn't wait for the answer, that's really difficult to work around.
I Do you ever tell a customer that something that they've tried on doesn't really suit them?
IR Yeah, all the time because I do want them to return, I don't want someone to go home with something for the sake of a sale, because that one sale might be profitable at the moment but if something doesn't suit a woman she will usually know, she'll know very soon, so either it will come back to the shop as a return or she'll just never come back to us and that is something that I would like to avoid.

4.2 **I** Do you get male customers as well as female customers?
IR Yes, we do, we do, and there'll be boyfriends and husbands and sons or son-in-laws.
I And are male customers any more difficult than female customers?
IR Yes and no. If they have shopped here before and if they know their wives' sizes, it will be very easy, also we have a very close relationship with our customers so we can actually,… for the most part we know who the woman is, so it will be easy enough for us to figure out what it is that she would love to have, in terms of colour and size and materials. If they are fairly new to this store, to the shop, it's harder, and very often we'll stand in as proxy for their wives or girlfriends and try things on and model them for the man to figure out what it is he would love to buy for her.
I Are you ever a difficult customer?
IR No, no, I hate difficult customers so no, not at all.
I Is shoplifting a problem here?
IR No, because it's a small shop and I think they are very quickly very uncomfortable, being watched. So no, it's not a big problem.
I But you do have shoplifters…
IR Yeah, yeah as everyone, and the shoplifting part is funny because all the merchants here know one another and we alert one another and that's what the phone is for, you know – man with green hat walking down the street he just tried to lift something, watch out for him.
I What are the best and worst sides of the job?
IR The best sides are community, a sense of belonging, New York is a big city and I feel I know everyone on the block, and that's unusual, so it has a small town feel at the same time. The worst side is feeling a little bit locked in sometimes, because you can't, unlike other jobs, you can't just walk out for a little five-minute break or go, you know, pick up your dry-cleaning around the corner, you have to wait until you can actually close the shop to do any other things in your life.

4.4 **Interviewer** Do you like being helped by a shop assistant when you are buying clothes?
Nick It depends what I am looking for, but quite often I can find it quite irritating.

I What irritates you most about shop assistants in clothes shops?

N When they recommend something that I am not really looking for.

Interviewer Do you like being helped by a shop assistant when you are buying clothes?

Mercedes Ah, no I don't, I like to browse myself because I know what I like.

I What irritates you most about shop assistants in clothes shops?

M When they're pushy and music really irritates me.

Interviewer Do you like being helped by a shop assistant when you are buying clothes?

Geri No, not really.

I What irritates you most about shop assistants in clothes shops?

G They always try to convince you that something that you are looking at is fantastic on you.

Interviewer Do you like being helped by a shop assistant when you are buying clothes?

Nadia Occasionally, if I cannot find my number, my size, but if I am just shopping around and… no.

I What irritates you most about shop assistants in clothes shops?

N When they're rude, when they don't really want to, like, do their job.

Interviewer Do you like being helped by a shop assistant when you are buying clothes?

Joey If I'm looking for a particular thing; if I'm not, I like to just shop, kind of, by myself.

I What irritates you most about shop assistants in clothes shops?

J When they're not that helpful, when they don't know what they are talking about.

5.1 **Interviewer** How old were you when you first learnt to ride?

Camilla Naprous I've ridden all my life really, but I started doing my stunts when I was eight years old.

I And who taught you how to ride?

C My father taught me mostly how to ride, but my brothers also taught me quite a lot too.

I What was the first stunt that you did?

C I did a thing called a Roman ride where you stand on two horses and they're connected between the heads with a tiny little strap and you gallop around.

I Was it dangerous?

C Oh, extremely dangerous, you know, especially if you're eight years old.

I Was your father worried that you might hurt yourself doing stunts?

C Not really because he's been a stuntman all his life and he's always wanted his children to start from an early age. It's best to start from an early age really because you have no fear.

I Have you ever been badly hurt doing a stunt?

C Touch wood, not yet.

I Do you need a special kind of horse for this kind of work?

C Oh God yeah, they've got to be so brave, they have got to be able to ride through a battlefield and not notice absolutely anything, explosions, anything.

I What kind of horses are these?

C These… this one is actually a Lusitano, he's a Portuguese horse and mainly we use Andalusians, which are a Spanish horse.

I When you work with actors can they usually already ride or do you need to teach them?

C Most of the time we have to teach them.

I And how long does that take?

C Sometimes production give you two days to teach them, sometimes you can have a month to teach them, it all depends on what time period they have, you know, with the actors' diaries and things.

5.2 **I** Who are easier to teach, men or women?

C When I teach actresses I find them a lot easier because they think about their safety, they're very good at listening, where some actors that you get hold of are quite macho, they kind of think they already know it.

I In a film how much of the riding do actors get to do themselves and how much is done by doubles?

C It all depends on the movie really, it depends on the director mostly, because some directors want their actors to ride non-stop. It all depends on the safety really, if something is too dangerous, then we have to bring a double in because we can't harm the actor. It all depends on the movie.

I Of all the actors you've worked with who was the best rider?

C It's got to be between Natalie Portman and Scarlett Johansson, that I shot *The Other Boleyn Girl* with. They did so well, they kind of competed against one other because they were doing similar roles, and they had a sisterly rivalry in the whole story, so that was an interesting movie to work on.

I Had they ridden before?

C Scarlett had ridden a little bit, because she did *The Horse Whisperer* when she was 12, but Natalie had never ridden before in her life.

I And how long did you spend with them before they were ready?

C I did quite well really. I had about a month to train them, so it was quite a long time for a movie so we had a lot of time between teaching them from start to finish.

I What film have you most enjoyed working on?

C I've just shot a movie called *Season of the Witch* with Nicholas Cage and that was good fun because we used the horses for the whole of the movie because it's a travelling story they're on it in every single scene.

5.4 **Interviewer** Do you have a favourite animal film or cartoon?

Daphne I guess I would have to say *The Lion King*.

I Why do you like it?

D It made me cry when I was a kid. It's a beautiful story.

I Would you like to work with animals?

D No, not really, no.

I Why not?

D I don't like every animal, I guess, and looking at them from a distance is enough. I wouldn't like to work with animals.

Interviewer Do you have a favourite animal film or cartoon?

Jade Tigger from *Winnie the Pooh*.

I Why do you like Tigger?

J I don't know, he's ridiculous and very energetic.

I Would you like to work with animals?

J No, I'm allergic to animals.

Interviewer Do you have a favourite animal film or cartoon?

Ash I like *Madagascar*.

I Why do you like it?

A Because it's got some interesting characters in it.

I Would you like to work with animals?

A I like dogs, but as a general rule, probably not.

I Why not?

A Because they're a bit messy and noisy.

Interviewer Do you have a favourite animal film or cartoon?

Elke Yes, I really enjoyed *Ice Age*, that was a good film.

I Why did you like it?

E It's really funny and it actually works for both adults and children, so it works on several levels for humour and you can all watch it as a family.

I Would you like to work with animals?

E That depends on the job. I mean the first thing that comes to mind is a vet and I think I would probably not like seeing these cute little animals suffer, so probably not. But if it was something,

you know, something really good, then yes, maybe.

Interviewer Do you have a favourite animal film or cartoon?

Ashley I sure do, *The Lion King*.

I Why?

A Because I've been to Africa so I thinks it's fun to watch the cartoon version of animals that I've seen.

I Would you like to work with animals?

A I don't think so.

I Why not?

A Because they smell.

6.1 **Interviewer** Is it common for criminals to confess to their crime?

Bob Fenton It's very rare for a criminal to confess. They all tell lies.

I Do you normally know when someone is lying?

B There is a body language attached to people who tell lies when they speak. One of the most common ones is eye contact so if you ask me a question and I replied, as soon as I finished my answer, I would look away, and then I would look back to see your response to my answer. A person telling the truth doesn't do that.

I Are men better liars than women or vice versa?

B That's a very good question. I would say that women are probably better liars than men. The problem is that most of the time they're interviewed by men, because there are still more men detectives than female detectives. And, of course, they try it on with the males whereas perhaps the best method for an interview with a female would be with a female detective.

I What is the most unbelievable excuse for a crime you have ever heard?

B I had a case once where a man was caught breaking into a house; he was actually stopped as he entered the house and he said that he was walking along the road and was thirsty, so he thought he would break into the house to get himself a glass of water. And his story was believed.

I Do you think that community service works better than prison for young offenders?

B Community service is a soft option in my opinion. I think that criminals will opt for that if they can and try and persuade a judge, or a magistrate, to give them a community service order rather than a custodial order, and I think they're just playing the system and hope that at the end of the day the penalty as such isn't strong and a lot of them will go back to crime immediately afterwards, if not during it.

6.2 **I** What's the most dangerous situation you've been in?

B I suppose the most dangerous one I was involved in was when I was in a police car and we were on an operation to catch some armed and dangerous men. These criminals were then seen and we followed them in their car – they had a car – we followed them and it ended up that they abandoned their car, actually on a bridge, and we then drove up and as they ran away, they actually had to come towards us because of the situation. But as they came past they fired at us both from the front of the vehicle and at the rear, so we had bullets in… I think we had three bullets in the front and two in the back. We then had to give chase on foot, very carefully I may add. The men then broke into a house, where they eventually came out after a few days, and gave themselves up. This incident ended up, obviously the men went to court and were all given life sentences, at the end of it I was awarded a gallantry medal, and had to go to Buckingham Palace, and I was presented with the medal by the Queen.

I In novels and on TV, detectives often have problems with their personal lives because of the hours they have to work and the stress of the job, do you think that is true in real life?

B Yes, policemen have one of the highest divorce rates in the country as an occupation. They tend to work hard and play hard, so they have long hours' work and when they finish they go to a restaurant and relax, and they don't go home. They talk with their pals and by the time they get home they hardly see any of their family, so I can understand why they have domestic problems.

I Would you recommend a career in the police?

B The simple answer is yes and I can illustrate that by saying that I have, in fact, five children – they all happen to be girls – but two of them, number two and number three, both themselves joined the police force because they realized I enjoyed it and they thought that would be a good career for them and I certainly wouldn't stop them pursuing that career, and of course the world being the world, they met policemen and married them and their husbands are both police officers.

6.4 **Interviewer** Who is your favourite fictional detective?

Steve I suspect *Columbo* is one of them, yeah.

I Why?

S Because he likes solving crimes and you think he's not going to solve them with his bumbling antics, but he actually does solve them in the end.

I Have you ever seen a crime being committed?

S No, I don't think I actually have, no.

Interviewer Who is your favourite fictional detective?

Sarah I think *Poirot*.

I Why?

S I like his moustache and he's a gentleman.

I Have you ever seen a crime being committed?

S I've seen someone trying to steal a bike.

Interviewer Who is your favourite fictional detective?

Ashley My favourite fictional detective is *Nancy Drew*.

I Why?

A My mum read all the books when she was younger, so when I read them it was nice to kind of read something that she'd already read.

I Have you ever seen a crime being committed?

A I guess so, yeah.

I What was it?

A I've seen people shoplifting and then running away from the store.

Interviewer Who is your favourite fictional detective?

Elke I really enjoyed *Miss Marple*, when I was younger I read a lot of Agatha Christie books and I thought she was a great character and we used to watch those films, Sunday afternoons and she was just a really good character. And then later on I also liked *Inspector Morse* because all the stories are set in Oxford and that's where I live, so it's very interesting.

I Have you ever seen a crime being committed?

E No, luckily not, no.

Interviewer Who is your favourite fictional detective?

Francesco My favourite fictional detective is *Sherlock Holmes*.

I Why?

F Because he's very intelligent, he uses his intelligence to solve very complex cases.

I Have you ever seen a crime being committed?

F Ah, yes I have, I've seen shoplifting being committed.

7.1 **Interviewer** What exactly do you do?

Sandy Kaiser I'm an American diplomat, which means I represent my country in other countries and I travel the world to do that. And in most countries you'll find an American Embassy, usually located in the capital, sometimes we may

have a consulate outside of the capital.

I What countries have you worked in?

S When I first became a diplomat I was lucky enough to be assigned to go to Brazil, which is a great, fascinating country. I learnt Portuguese and I went to Brasilia, the capital, which is in the middle of the country, which is a new capital – fairly new capital – and then I was lucky enough to go to Rio de Janeiro, so I saw the two extremes of Brazil. I got to dance in the Brazilian carnival, it was one of the high points, I think, of my diplomatic career, and wear a fancy costume, that was great. After that I was on my way to the former Yugoslavia, to Sarajevo and so I studied Serbo-Croatian language and I was three days away from going there when the war broke out in Bosnia, which put an end to my assignment, and unfortunately I never... my Serbian never really recovered from that.

I So then where did you go?

S Instead I ended up going to Estonia at the time of the fall of the Soviet Union, and was there from 1991 to 94 – that was a fantastic time, a very difficult language for an English speaker to learn. I didn't ever really become fluent, but I could speak a few words and phrases. After that I went to Germany and I spent four years in the Rhineland. After that back to the United States, then after that I went to Greece, and before I went to Greece I studied Greek language for a year, which was very interesting for an English speaker because we have so many words in English that come from Greek.

I And after that?

S Then after that I went to Denmark where people have very high level of English language ability and I did not have to study Danish, although I did pick up a few phrases. And then from Denmark I've I've come here, so, yeah, I've studied a lot of languages, most of them in the European family, in fact all of them.

7.2 **I** How long have you been in London?

S I've been here about nine months.

I How does being in London compare with the other countries you've been to?

S Oh yeah, for a diplomat, London is the best, I mean. I think for an American diplomat it is one of the closest relationships we have in the world, and so it's an honour to come here. As President Obama said recently it still is very much the special relationship, it's absolutely centre to everything America wants to accomplish in the world, so it's a wonderful place to be.

I What do you like best about the UK?

S I like very much the British... the British village, the way a village functions in Britain, the way that the villages have evolved over time has been in a way that permits you to live perhaps on the edge of the countryside but yet still be able to walk to the pharmacy or walk to a grocery store, and I really like that. I think that is a big difference and it's something that I think Americans can learn from.

I What don't you like about life in the UK?

S I come from the Western part of America, which is the most lightly populated part of the United States, and I am used to having lots of space and lots of, you know, big open vistas. I... there aren't that many places in Britain that you could really have that sense of being alone in a wilderness. One big thing that strikes me in terms of difference is the cost of living is very very high here. In America we tend to earn a bit more for similar professions and we pay a lot less for rent, for groceries, for almost everything.

I What problems do you think a British person would have going to live in the US?

S I think there would be aspects to America that would probably be puzzling, especially when you feel familiar with the culture because in Britain, of

course, people watch a lot of American television, and even though they know that what you see on TV is not true, somehow there is a part of your brain that buys it anyway. And so I feel when British people come to America they're often pleasantly surprised because we're not as violent or as extreme as television shows us to be. They... I think most British people when they come to America actually feel very comfortable, perhaps a little relieved too.

7.4 **Interviewer** Do you find it easier to understand British or American speakers?

Elke Well, I'm from Germany and I learnt English at school in Germany, and we learnt British English. And any English or American films we saw would always be dubbed so you don't really get a chance to hear much of American English. And also British pronunciation is quite sharp and crisp. So maybe being German that comes a bit easier to me.

I Would you prefer to live in the US or in the UK?

E That's quite a difficult question to answer because all my knowledge of America comes from one trip to New York and the rest comes from the media or books. I mean the weather obviously would probably be a lot nicer in America or certain parts of America compared to Britain, but I've lived here for ten years now and I like it and I enjoy it. I have friends here. I mean I couldn't see myself living in America now for that reason.

Interviewer Do you find it easier to understand British or American speakers?

José I think I prefer English people because they speak more slowly than the Americans. And they make a few pauses when they speak.

I Would you prefer to live in the US or in the UK?

J Maybe in the US – fine weather, bigger country, lots of people from everywhere in the world.

Interviewer Do you find it easier to understand British or American speakers?

Francesco I find it easier to understand British speakers because I learnt British English in school when I was in Italy.

I Would you prefer to live in the US or in the UK?

F I have lived in both countries, but I think Britain is easier for me because of the similarities with Italian culture in the European, sort of, continent.

Interviewer Do you find it easier to understand British or American speakers?

Daniela I would say American English because I'm from Sweden and we have a lot of shows and – TV shows, that is – and movies from America. And you hear it more often because you don't really dub the shows in Sweden so it's a natural part of life, I would say.

I Would you prefer to live in the US or in the UK?

D I would say at the moment the US. I'm here looking for a job in New York; I lived here last year too. But when it comes to the long run I would say the UK. I definitely prefer the political system there. And I think it's more similar to Sweden. I would definitely prefer that.

The British Isles

N

Over 1000m
500 - 1000 m
200 - 500m
100 - 200m
Under 100m
Below sea level

Shetland Islands

Unst
Yell
Mainland
Foula
Bressay
Lerwick
Sumburgh Head

North Atlantic Ocean

North Sea

Orkney Islands
Sandsay
Mainland
Stronsay
Hoy
S. Ronaldsay
Kirkwall
Pentland Firth
JOHN O'GROATS
Wick

Butt of Lewis
Cape Wrath
Lewis
Stornoway
Harris
Ullapool
North Uist
Grimsay
Uig
Skye
South Uist
Barra
LOCH NESS
Inverness
Moray Firth
Fraserburgh
Aberdeen
Ben Macdhui
BALMORAL
Rhum
Fort William
Ben Nevis
Grampian Mountains
Montrose
Mull
Oban
Dundee
Jura
Loch Lomond
Perth
SCOTLAND
Islay
Stirling
Firth of Forth
Glasgow
EDINBURGH
Clyde
Cambeltown
Kilmarnock
Arran
Firth of Clyde
Southern Uplands
Holy Island
Chevion Hills

Malin Head
Giant's Causeway
Dumfries
Newcastle upon Tyne
Aran Island
Rossan Point
Londonderry
Stranraer
HADRIAN'S WALL
Gateshead
Sunderland
Donegal
Omagh
Antrim Mountains
Carlisle
Middlesbrough
Erris Head
Enniskillen
NORTHERN
CUMBRIA
LAKE DISTRICT
North Yorkshire Moors
Scarborough
Sligo
IRELAND
Grasmere
Ambleside
Filey Bay
Flamborough Head
Achill Head
Scafell Pike
Hawkshead
Yorkshire Dales
Achill Island
Slieve Donard
Douglas
Morecambe Bay
Lancaster
Yorkshire Wolds
Dundalk
Dundalk Bay
Isle of Man
Leeds
York
Hull
REPUBLIC
Irish Sea
Bolton
Spurn Head
OF
Manchester
Lincolnshire Wolds
Grimsby
IRELAND
Holyhead
Liverpool
Salford
Sheffield
Galway
Dublin
Anglesey
Colwyn Bay
Chester
Peak District
Nottingham
The Wash
Aran Islands
Caernarfon Bay
SNOWDONIA
Stoke -on-Trent
HARDWICK HALL
Loop Head
Limerick
Snowdon
Oswestry
Derby
The Broads
Tralee Bay
Wicklow Mountains
Stafford
Leicester
Norwich
Tralee
Wicklow Head
Aberystwyth
Cambrian Mts
Birmingham
The Fens
Killarney
Waterford
Cardigan Bay
Coventry
ENGLAND
Cambridge
Carrauntoohill
Rosslare
WALES
Northampton
Ipswich
Bray Head
Cork
Fishguard
Stratford-upon-Avon
Barrington
Orford Ness
Bantry
Cork Harbour
St. David's Head
PEMBROKESHIRE COAST
BRECON BEACONS
Cotswold Hills
Oxford
HERTFORD-SHIRE
Colchester
The Naze
Mizen Head
Old Head of Kinsale
Milford Haven
Carmarthen Bay
Newport
Chiltern Hills
Watford
Bantry Bay
Lundy
CARDIFF
Bristol
Reading
LONDON
Greenwich
Bath
Windsor
KENT
Bristol Channel
STONEHENGE
North Downs
Canterbury
Exmoor
LONGLEAT
Salisbury Plain
South Foreland
Glastonbury
LEEDS CASTLE
Dover
New Forest
Southampton
South Downs
Dungeness
Bodmin Moor
DARTMOOR
Bournemouth
Portsmouth
GLYNDEBOURNE
Beachy Head
Newquay
Exeter
Lyme Bay
Brighton
Plymouth
Portland Bill
Isle of Wight
Selsey Bill
Mevagissey
Start Point
Land's End
Penzance
Lizard Point
Isles of Scilly
English Channel
Alderney
Channel Islands
Guernsey
Sark
Jersey
FRANCE

North Atlantic Ocean

Thames Estuary

0   150 miles
0   200 kilometres

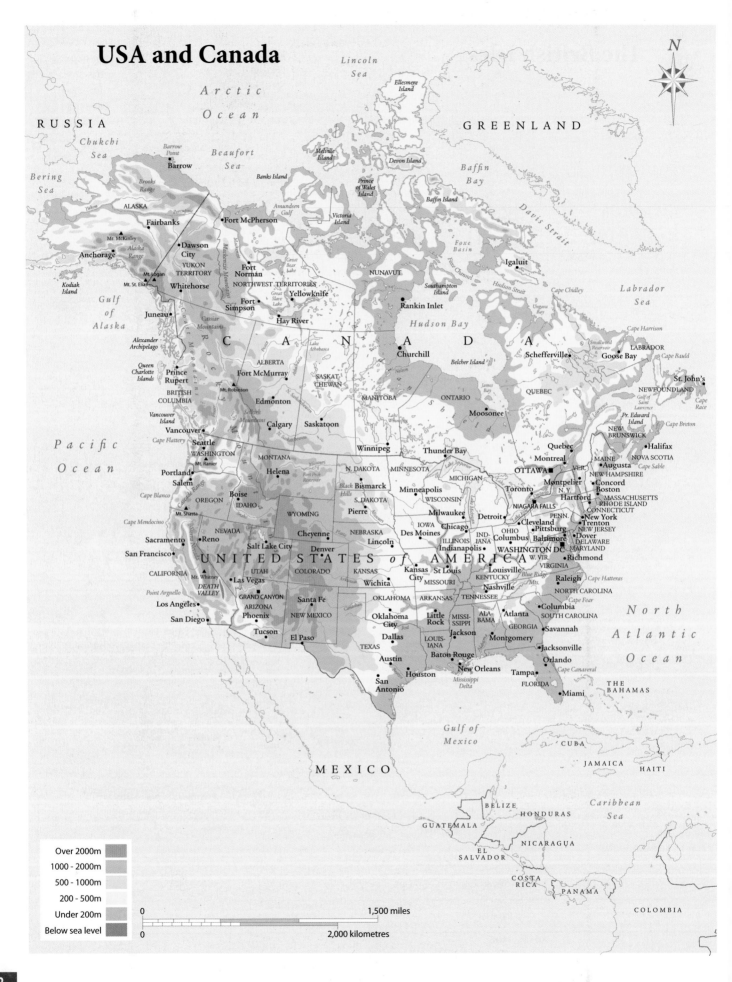

USA and Canada

N

RUSSIA

GREENLAND

Chukchi Sea

Bering Sea

Arctic Ocean

Lincoln Sea

Ellesmere Island

Devon Island

Melville Island

Banks Island

Beaufort Sea

Barrow Point

•Barrow

Brooks Range

ALASKA

Yukon

•Fairbanks

▲Mt. McKinley

Anchorage

Alaska Range

Mt. Logan▲
Mt. St. Elias▲

•Dawson City

YUKON TERRITORY

•Whitehorse

Kodiak Island

Gulf of Alaska

Juneau•

Porcupine

•Fort McPherson

Amundsen Gulf

Victoria Island

Prince of Wales Island

Baffin Island

Baffin Bay

Foxe Basin

Southampton Island

Davis Strait

•Igaluit

Labrador Sea

Cape Chidley

Mackenzie Mountains

Fort Norman

Mackenzie River

Great Bear Lake

NORTHWEST TERRITORIES

Fort Simpson

•Yellowknife

Hay River•

Great Slave Lake

Lake Athabasca

NUNAVUT

•Rankin Inlet

Hudson Bay

Rock Channel

Ungava Bay

Smallwood Reservoir

Cape Harrison

Cassiar Mountains

C A N A D A

•Churchill

Belcher Island

James Bay

Scheffeville•

LABRADOR

•Goose Bay

Cape Bauld

Alexander Archipelago

Queen Charlotte Islands

Prince Rupert•

BRITISH COLUMBIA

▲Mt. Robinson

ALBERTA

•Fort McMurray

Edmonton•

•Calgary

SASKAT-
CHEWAN

•Saskatoon

MANITOBA

Nelson

Lake Winnipeg

ONTARIO

•Moosonee

QUEBEC

•Quebec

NEWFOUNDLAND

Pr. Edward Island

Cape Race

Gulf of Saint Lawrence

•St. John's

Cape Breton

Vancouver Island

Vancouver•

Seattle•

WASHINGTON

▲Mt. Ranier

MONTANA

Missouri

Fort Peck Reservoir

N. DAKOTA

Bismarck•

•Winnipeg

•Thunder Bay

Lake Superior

MICHIGAN

Toronto•

NIAGARA FALLS

Lake Huron

Lake Ontario

Montreal•

OTTAWA■

Montpelier•

VER.

MAINE

•Augusta

Cape Sable

NEW BRUNSWICK

•Halifax

NOVA SCOTIA

NEW HAMPSHIRE

•Concord

Boston•

MASSACHUSETTS

RHODE ISLAND

CONNECTICUT

Cape Flattery

Portland•

Salem•

OREGON

Cape Blanco

Boise•

IDAHO

Cascade Range

WYOMING

Cheyenne•

S. DAKOTA

Pierre•

Black Hills

MINNESOTA

Minneapolis•

WISCONSIN

•Milwaukee

Chicago•

Detroit•

Cleveland•

Pittsburg•

Columbus•

OHIO

IND-
IANA

N.Y.

Hartford•

New York•

Trenton•

NEW JERSEY

•Dover

DELAWARE

Cape Mendocino

▲Mt. Shasta

NEVADA

Reno•

Sacramento•

San Francisco•

Point Arguello

UNITED STATES of AMERICA

Salt Lake City•

UTAH

Denver•

COLORADO

NEBRASKA

Lincoln•

IOWA

Des Moines•

ILLINOIS

Indianapolis•

Platte

Kansas City•

St Louis•

WASHINGTON DC■

MARYLAND

Richmond•

W. VIR.

VIRGINIA

Louisville•

KENTUCKY

Blue Ridge Mts.

Raleigh•

Cape Hatteras

CALIFORNIA

▲Mt. Whitney

Las Vegas•

DEATH VALLEY

GRAND CANYON■

ARIZONA

Phoenix•

Santa Fe•

NEW MEXICO

KANSAS

Wichita•

OKLAHOMA

Oklahoma City•

Arkansas

Canadian

ARKANSAS

Little Rock•

MISSOURI

TENNESSEE

Nashville•

NORTH CAROLINA

Columbia•

SOUTH CAROLINA

Cape Fear

Atlanta•

GEORGIA

Savannah•

Los Angeles•

San Diego•

•Tucson

El Paso•

TEXAS

Dallas•

Austin•

Houston•

San Antonio•

LOUIS-
IANA

MISSI-
SSIPPI

Jackson•

Baton Rouge•

New Orleans•

Mississippi Delta

ALA-
BAMA

Montgomery•

Jacksonville•

Orlando•

Tampa•

FLORIDA

•Miami

Cape Canaveral

North Atlantic Ocean

Pacific Ocean

Gulf of Mexico

CUBA

JAMAICA

HAITI

THE BAHAMAS

M E X I C O

BELIZE

GUATEMALA

EL SALVADOR

HONDURAS

NICARAGUA

COSTA RICA

PANAMA

Caribbean Sea

COLOMBIA